D1580629

BATTLE
FOR THE
MIND

Also available in the "How to" series:

Effective Evangelism	Ben Davies
Enjoying God's Grace	Terry Virgo
Growing Up as a Christian	Roger Day
Handling Your Money	John Houghton
Joining the Church	Richard Haydon-Knowell
Knowing God's Will	Phil Rogers
Leading a Housegroup	Richard Haydon-Knowell
Learning to Worship	Phil Rogers
Praying the Lord's Prayer	Terry Virgo
Presenting Jesus in the Open Air	Mike Sprenger
Seeking the Kingdom	John Hosier

For further information on the "How to" series and New Frontiers International, please write to New Frontiers International, 21-23 Clarendon Villas, Hove, Brighton, East Sussex, BN3 3RE.

How to...
STUDY SERIES

BATTLE
FOR THE
MIND

DAVID HOLDEN

NEW FRONTIERS INTERNATIONAL

WORD PUBLISHING
WORD (UK) Ltd
Milton Keynes, England
WORD AUSTRALIA
Kilsyth, Victoria, Australia
WORD COMMUNICATIONS LTD
Vancouver, B.C., Canada
STRUIK CHRISTIAN BOOKS (PTY) LTD
Maitland, South Africa
ALBY COMMERCIAL ENTERPRISES PTE LTD
Balmoral Road, Singapore
CHRISTIAN MARKETING NEW ZEALAND LTD
Havelock North, New Zealand
JENSCO LTD
Hong Kong
SALVATION BOOK CENTRE
Malaysia

BATTLE FOR THE MIND

© David Holden 1990.
Published by Word (UK) Ltd/New Frontiers.

All rights reserved. No part of this publication may be reproduced or
transmitted in any form or by any means, electronic or mechanical,
including photocopy, recording, or any information storage or retrieval
system, without permission in writing from the publisher.

ISBN 0-85009-190-X (Australia ISBN 1-86258-112-6)

Unless otherwise indicated, Scripture quotations are from the New
International Version (NIV).
© 1978 New York International Bible Society

Typesetting by ALMAC, Northampton and printed and bound in
Great Britain by Cox & Wyman Ltd., Reading.

90 91 92 93 94 95 10 9 8 7 6 5 4 3 2 1

FOREWORD

The "How to" series has been published with a definite purpose in view. It provides a set of workbooks suitable either for housegroups or individuals who want to study a particular Bible theme in a practical way. The goal is not simply to look up verses and fill in blank spaces on the page, but to fill in gaps in our lives and so increase our fruitfulness and our knowledge of God.

Peter wrote his letters to "stimulate wholesome thinking" (2 Peter 3:1). He required his readers to think as well as read! We hope the training manual approach of this book will have the same effect. *Stop, think, apply* and *act* are key words.

If you are using the book on your own, we suggest you work through the chapters systematically, Bible at your side and pen in hand. If you are doing it as a group activity, it is probably best to do all the initial reading and task work before the group sessions – this gives more time for discussion on key issues which may be raised.

Unless otherwise stated, all quotations from the Bible are from the New International Version which you are, in the main, encouraged to use when you fill in the study material.

Terry Virgo
Series Editor

SPECIAL THANKS

I would like to express my deepest thanks to my friend and colleague **David Rigby**, who spent many, many hours working through my notes to ensure that this book could come into being.

David Holden

NEW FRONTIERS INTERNATIONAL is a team ministry led by Terry Virgo and involved in planting and equipping churches according to New Testament principles with a view to reaching this generation with the gospel of the Kingdom. They are also responsible for a wide range of conferences, training programmes and the production of printed and audio teaching materials.

Contents

Introduction

Defeated by temptation? Lack of growth and fruitfulness? Most of your problems are in your mind.

You are still thinking the old way. You have been born again by the Spirit of God, but nothing much has happened in your mind. The potential that you have to overcome the lies of the enemy and to live a victorious life remains just potential.

Are you still dominated by fears from the past? Do you suffer anxiety, do you find that you cannot shake off self-pity or a sense of rejection? Are you still tyrannized by lustful thoughts? A sorry state! What is worse, it can go on for years!

This problem is not simply associated with young people or young Christians, it is amazingly widespread. Some Christians live their lives in a pit of permanent defeat. How sad when it need not be so.

We are surrounded by pressures which, if succumbed to, influence our minds and our thinking in ungodly ways. Sometimes subtly, sometimes more directly, many people use the powerful communication ability of the media to put their priorities and their message across and to influence our minds away from God.

Our background and our upbringing, our friends at school and our favourite teachers all influenced us in the past. The question is: what is the dominant influence on your mind today as a Christian?

This book aims to take hold of the defeated minds, the easily diverted minds and the plain empty-heads and help you begin to reach out for all the potential that is yours in Christ and make it your own.

This is an exciting and very radical opportunity. The power of God which is at work within you can change your thinking!

Even more radical is the possibility that, having begun along this road of renewal of the mind, you will be increasingly equipped to help others.

Now that's something else!

PART ONE: WHY RENEW YOUR MIND?

Chapter 1   HOW VITAL IS THE RENEWED MIND?

Our Aim

The Word of God is absolutely clear: it is vital that as Christians we change the way we think. The Bible says it is essential if we are to live victorious Christian lives. We should be in no doubt about the vital role our minds have in shaping us as people.

Let us take one particular verse as an example.

Write out the first phrase of Proverbs 23:7. (If you are using the NIV, the marginal translation is actually more correct.)

For as he thinks within himself so he is

To reinforce the message, let us rewrite it in its most basic form so that we get the full impact of it. Fill in the missing words:

As you *THINK* ... so you *ARE*

This is why it is so vital for your mind to be renewed. It is what is floating around in your mind which will affect the way you behave on a daily basis.

The way you think affects your attitudes, your hopes and your fears. The way you think affects the way you react to people, the way you speak to others, and how you handle your job and its pressures. It affects the way you raise your family if you are a parent, and the way you relate to your own father and mother.

Write down a couple of recent examples that you can remember from your own experience where your thinking caused problems for you when it slipped out in your speech or in your actions:

Speech: *Sarcasm & bitchiness at work*

....

....

Actions: ....

On edge around men

....

Thoughts always end up affecting our actions. You can think something and sooner or later it will infiltrate into your behaviour. That influence can be for good or it can be for bad, depending on the way you think. The way you act depends on the way you think.

Here is a typical example for single young men. One day, you meet a gorgeous girl. A thought comes into your mind along the lines of: ''Wow! How tremendous!'' You've started something and it can end up in a walk down the aisle! You have to be careful with thoughts.

When I met my wife for the first time, the first thought that came into my mind was ''Terrific!'' I tried to rebuke it, but it wouldn't go away. It was a good thought, a nice thought, and it led to action.

Conversely, it can work the other way. Here is an example from my schooldays. I am standing in Woolworths on the way home from school. No one is particularly looking at what I'm doing and there are the rows of sweets arranged along the counter in front of me. The thought comes, just a little thought: ''Go on, do it.'' I used to have a black gabardine raincoat with huge pockets in it, just to increase the temptation.

The tragedy of people hooked on shoplifting is that it all started one day just like that: the little thought became an action.

Remember the little catch phrase, "I did it without thinking" beloved of schoolchildren – and others! Think through the sequence of events carefully – is it possible?

Possible	
Impossible	

Consider even habitual actions. There is always a thought, even a very spontaneous and quick one, before the action is undertaken. The mind has to say to the body, "Move!" There's a temptation, then there's a thought and then the action comes.

12

It is vital to renew the mind. As Christians we must take control of our actions. Therefore, we need to take control of our minds. Our minds have to know how to deal with the daily barrage of thoughts if we are to overcome sin.

The Process

Let us look at a key verse for the subject of the mind, one I am sure many of you are familiar with.

Write out the first half of Romans 12:2:

Do not conform any longer to the pattern of this world, but be transformed by the renewing of your mind.

The word used in the Greek for "transformed" is the same word which forms the root of our word "metamorphis". It is the same word as Paul uses in 2 Corinthians 3:18 where he speaks about us as Christians being transformed into the likeness of Christ with ever-increasing glory.

Take a dictionary and look at the definition of "transform". Now with that information and remembering the Greek root in "metamorphis" tick the description below you think is most accurate:

to be affected by, to have regard to, to acknowledge ☐

to be influenced by, to adapt behaviour, to adjust ☐

to reorientate, to be convinced, to alter aspects ☐

to revolutionize, to turn right around, to remould ✓

Now that's interesting, isn't it? We're not just to be affected or influenced by our Christian faith, we're to see a *revolution* occur in our thinking.

If you like you could rephrase Romans 12:2 to say something like "be transformed, be rearranged, be totally changed, be completely and utterly removed and moved on".

(i) The process is gradual.

The Bible says some dramatic things about what happens when we become Christians. For most of us it takes some time to grasp all that God has done in that rebirth, because such a lot happens without us fully realizing it at first.

Here are just some of the truths about your rebirth:

He has rescued us from the dominion of darkness and *brought us into the kingdom of the Son he loves* (Col 1:13)

The old has gone, *and the new* has come! (2 Cor 5:17)

All are justified freely by *his grace through the redemption that came by Christ Jesus* (Rom 3:24)

To all who received Him, to those who believed in His name, He gave *the right to become children of God* (John 1:12)

If anyone is in Christ, he is *a new creation* (2 Cor 5:17)

The Bible says that when you receive a new heart, you receive a new spirit, a new nature. You have a new song in your heart and on your lips, but nowhere do the scriptures say you receive a new mind.

What it does say is that *you are to renew your mind*. The implication is that the old mind you used to have is still there! Some of us might feel a little disappointed with that; perhaps we were hoping for a new mind with about twice as much I.Q.! What a shame!

This is a vital lesson to learn: a new mind didn't just drop out of heaven. We didn't wake up on the first day of our new Christian life with a mind that had been replaced in the night. We soon discover that instant holiness and instant righteous thinking is not how it is, is it?

The good news is that it's the same old mind, but *the process of change* can begin. It's going to be changed, it's going to be renewed, it's going to be transformed. For most of us that process can certainly be quicker than it is, but it is still a process.

2 Corinthians 5:17

(ii) The process is from the world.

A transformation involves two extremes, two sides: what we are transformed from, and what we are transformed into.

The renewing of our mind will transform us from the pattern of ....
.... *this world* .... (Rom 12:2)

This is radical! Sadly, many Christians, when they are first born again, are placed under a very legalistic way of living. The intentions are good and honourable – to help them develop Christian character – but the result is usually ineffective. This is because they only deal with the outward appearance and not with the mind.

Legalism has nothing to do with the way you think, but rather the way you dress, the way you behave, the sort of films, television and music which is "acceptable", and the achievement of goals in terms of meetings attended, chapters of the Bible read, etc.

Of course the way you dress will reflect your background, the way you are and the way you think. For example, punks adopted their distinctive style of dress out of a spirit of rebellion. Something within was rebelling and it affected the way they dressed. Later it became fashionable for a lot of people.

When someone like that is saved the idea is not that he or she conforms to the way Christians dress, but rather to the way Christians think. As that transformation in the mind away from the world's thinking occurs, it will probably affect the way that person dresses. You will see an outworking of a changed mind. We don't impose a law on dress, but changed dress will be the fruit which we will later see from a changed mind.

Review: This is so important and fundamental a concept for the renewing of your mind that you should stop here and review. Have you grasped the difference between the outward "law" and the inward working of grace on your mind?

(iii) The process is to link you into God's purposes.

The second phrase of Romans 12:2 says:

Then you will ..... *be able to test & approve what God's will is – his good, pleasing & perfect will*

15

Guidance is another area where Christians seem to struggle. We can be very woolly over guidance, and there are Christians around who still resort to sticking pins onto the pages of their Bible.

Here is a *key* to guidance. The reason many of us struggle with guidance is that we haven't been renewed in the way that we think. Our minds are cluttered up with all sorts of other thoughts and jargon, what other people think and how they will react, so that we cannot discern the direction God is leading us, and what He is saying.

As our mind is renewed and transformed onto Godly ways of thinking and looking at situations, we will discover that our minds are more settled and more confident. In that context the way we live will be increasingly clear and decisions will have less uncertainty to them. There will still be calls to steps of faith, but we will know more clearly that those steps are the call of God.

Look again at Romans 12:2 and finish the following paraphrase:

Let your mind be renewed, then you will know ....*God's*........

will for your life – what is ....*good*........ and ....*pleasing*........

and ....*perfect*........ for you in Him.

Is Your Mind Uncontrolled?

Many Christians are hooked up about their sin "problems": their habits, their behaviour, their appearance, etc. They are trying to change their "self" without ever dealing with the root problem.

> The root problem with sin is the way we ....*think*........

So change the way you think and you will begin to deal with the sin problems that remain in your life.

God's ultimate purpose is for us all to become like Jesus. That's not just a glib phrase to be looked at and acknowledged, we have got to start thinking the way He thinks. When we begin to think about issues the way Jesus does, we know we are becoming more like Him. If you are to be changed to be like Jesus, you must first begin to think like Him in order that, as a result, your character and actions might be reflective of Him.

For that to begin to happen we need controlled minds. Is your mind under control?

Here are some examples of the uncontrolled mind at work.

(i) Stress and anxiety

Some doctors estimate as much as 75% of their waiting-room patients may have a physical problem that is actually a product of their mind and their thoughts. The mind is a powerful instrument.

For example, the Jones family have the flu and you visit them. A little thought comes in: ''If I visit them I might catch it.'' By the time you're on the doorstep ringing the bell your legs ache, your back aches and you feel all hot and sweaty.

Take another example: a stressful thought can have repercussions that are physical. An anxious thought can lead to illness. People suffer like that, even Christians, because their minds are uncontrolled.

Now by no means all fearful and anxious thoughts will result in such conditions, but it illustrates the devastation an uncontrolled mind can reap. And, anyway, who wants to be in the grip of fear and anxiety?

(ii) Sexual temptation

With David and Bathsheba (2 Samuel 11) sin didn't begin with an action, it began with a thought. In fact, it began with a thought in an ill-disciplined mind. David should have been leading his troops on the battlefield, his adrenalin surging and his mind razor-sharp. Instead he was wandering around his palace, dissipating his time in idle thoughts and idle behaviour. In that environment he was very vulnerable. The sight of a beautiful woman sent his thought life pounding down uncontrolled tracks.

What about lust? That's a massive problem for a lot of people, and not just amongst the men either. That whole area of lust, pornography, fantasy and sexual bombardment from the world gains its entry via our thinking. That is where the attack is concentrated – in your mind.

(iii) Cynicism

Here is another big one for us, especially us British. We are a cynical race of people. It's certainly something most British Christians need to be transformed from. We are brought up in a cynical way of thinking through

17

school and this is continually reinforced through television and the media generally throughout our adult lives. This is an enormous barrier to Christian thinking – it affects the way we think, the way we analyse situations and the way we respond to others.

Cynicism can be devastating to our speech and personality. It starts in the mind, and can run uncontrolled.

(iv) Negativism
Perhaps related to cynicism, negativism is such a large part of many Christians' background. It can be really damaging. Parents can speak persistently negative things to their children and it takes root in their thinking. Maybe you were always bottom or almost bottom of the class, and even as an adult you have never been encouraged in your abilities. What happens over the years is that you develop a habitually negative way of thinking, especially about yourself.

(v) Self-pity
Low self-image can lead to frequent pity-parties. The truth is that God has never said anything to make you feel self-pity or to have a low self-image. Actually, He does the opposite, so where on earth did this way of thinking come from? An unrenewed mind! It is contrary to the Word of God, so we need to deal with it.

(vi) Anger
Some people have terribly big problems when it comes to anger. It begins in the way you think. Many people manage to hold their anger to their thoughts. In that way they control their actions, and they don't retaliate verbally or physically, but the thought is there. Big and ugly.

For some it does sometimes spill over into verbal abuse and even physical reaction, but it still starts the same way – in an uncontrolled mind.

(vii) Fears
Some people have fears that are based on traumatic experiences of the past, but the uncontrolled mind has allowed that trauma to run riot, to walk all over your everyday experience.

Imagine the typical scene: a child of four or five years old is walking along the road and a great, enormous dog comes bounding up, all bright-eyed and full of fun. The tail swishes, the dog barks and the child is terrified of this overwhelming animal. A moment in time, a fearsome thought and it's the beginning of a lifelong fear of dogs that affects that person's behaviour and personality.

The good news is that the effect of that trauma on our minds and actions can be erased as our minds are renewed in Christ.

Renewing the mind is absolutely vital for every Christian, however much or little you have been able to identify yourself with those examples given above. It is essential because it will affect our whole life style and our ability to walk in the ways God has prepared for us for His glory.

Chapter 2   THE STATE OF YOUR MIND

In this chapter we will be looking at the two states of mind: firstly, before you were in Christ, and, secondly, now you are in Christ. Finally, we will explore the dynamics of the change from one state to the other.

1. Before You Were in Christ

Romans 1 is a chapter all about men and women away from Christ. Men and women, born in Adam, have an inclination towards belief and an awareness that, out there, there is a living God, yet have turned away from God and have attempted to live by their own knowledge and power.

Look at this crucial verse for the subject of the mind – Romans 1:28:

Since they did not think it worth while ....*to retain the knowledge of God, he gave them over to a depraved mind, to do what ought not to be done*....

There is an awesome phrase which Paul keeps repeating in Romans 1. Look at verses 24, 26 and 28. What is that repeated phrase?

God gave them over to...

God made His judgement on the way they were thinking, on the way their minds were working. He said in effect, "O.K. Enough is enough. I give you over. Have your own way then and reap its fruit." So then, before we were in Christ our minds were depraved, bent towards thinking improper, unclean and self-destroying thoughts. Our minds were full of sin.

It is, for those outside of Christ, a natural process. You do not have to train children to argue. You do not have to teach little brothers and sisters to fight over toys. They do it naturally. Naughtiness comes with an amazing sense of ease and ability. They seem made for it!

Now look at Ephesians 2:3. This verse is talking about our state, our condition, before we were in Christ.

What did we gratify? ..... *the cravings of our sinful nature* .....

What did we follow? *its desires + thoughts* .....

See how important it is that we understand this. It doesn't matter what sort of home you were brought up in. You may have been brought up in a Christian home, your dad may even have been an elder. Or you may not have known who your parents were. That is all irrelevant. By nature, by your very being on this planet, you would naturally indulge the desires of your mind.

Turn to Ephesians 4:17-18:

How did we live? *was separated from the life of God - darkened in their understanding* .....

Before we were in Christ we were darkened in our understanding and separated from the life of God. Our hearts were hardened.

To give you an example, some while ago a friend and I were witnessing to a group from CND. They were into the peace movement in a very big way and totally committed to it. You have never heard such a verbally violent reaction as we were given. We just talked about Jesus and suddenly peace was gone! They may have been proclaiming peace without the bomb, but their hearts were hardened to the claims of Jesus that real peace only comes through Him. The reaction of hardened, rebellious hearts was as vehement as could be.

The next verse to look at is Colossians 1:21:What was our relationship to God in our minds?

enemies .....

We don't like to think like this. It's not comfortable. But the Bible is clear that before we were in Christ our minds were darkened and our thinking was futile. There is a sense in which we were kept away from God – alienated and enemies – because of our thinking. You will see the same idea expressed in 2 Corinthians 4:3.

Before you were in Christ Satan hung a veil over your thinking, distorting and denying the truth of God. He blinded you from seeing things as you ought to see them.

Nevertheless ...

Romans 1 reminds us that even looking at creation alone it is plain to see that there is a God. The "argument from design" (as it is known) is a very powerful one. Colleges and universities are full of people doing philosophy and similar subjects because deep inside all of us there is this half-acknowledged cry that there must be a God. Go to any campus and you'll find students earnestly discussing the origin of things. Most, the more honest anyway, would admit it takes a very big leap of faith indeed to believe it all just came about by chance.

Look at Titus 1:15. Fill in the missing words:

In fact, both their ....minds.... and ...consciences...... are corrupted.

The Bible is very clear that you have a conscience, too. Not only can I discover God in creation, but I can see Him reflected in my conscience. I knew what was right and wrong before I was a Christian, didn't you?

All that talk in the sixties and seventies about free living and casual sex being all right was really a corrupted conscience battling against itself, proclaiming loudly to drown out the conviction that actually the truth was otherwise.

Before you were in Christ you had a conscience. It was there, bent, corrupted, defiled, weak, easily conned and twisted, but still there. Many people are easily led and allow their consciences to be easily overrun.

For example, the way that homosexuality has been presented in schools, particularly in London in recent years, has defiled consciences that were already there.

The argument goes like this (to paraphrase): "On the right, children, we have a man, and here on the left, children, is a woman. Full manhood and full femininity – and in between, children, are different mixtures of manhood and femininity. What you have to do, children, is find out where on the spectrum you fit."

The issue, of course, is that this is suggestive. The poor child in the classroom has never been asked to think like that before. He was a boy and she was a girl. "Now", the boy thinks, "am I fully man? Perhaps I have a good dose of femininity in me. I don't know."

I believe a lot of people get into things they never really assented to. They never had any intention of touching these things, but because a process of thinking got hold of them, and their minds were uncontrolled and their consciences darkened, they were unable to resist.

Have you ever wondered how people seem so incapable sometimes of understanding the gospel? It's so simple, yet they seem as thick as two planks! I sat through gospel service after gospel service, rebellious and angry. Surprise, surprise! I didn't understand any of it. It was alien to me because my mind was veiled to the truth. I remained alienated and far from Him with my mind the playground of God's enemy, Satan.

You may say that you were a pretty decent sort of person before you were a Christian. The problem is God doesn't just look at the actions, He looks at the *thoughts* of a man, too. Jesus said even to look on a woman in an adulterous way is to commit adultery. Just the thought is enough. God sees our motives, and our thoughts, and we are full of sin, through and through.

2. Now You Are in Christ

Something tremendously exciting happens when you are born again. God lifts the veil. For the first time in your life the light of God begins to penetrate your darkened mind. The veil over your understanding is lifted. It's as if the gateway to your mind is swung open by the Lord Himself and He steps inside.

Suddenly, you understand things. Scripture verses spring to life, the songs in the meetings take on a meaning you'd missed before and you know heaven has invaded your thinking.

Look at God's tremendous promise in Hebrews 10:16:

Where will God put His laws? ... *in our hearts* ...

Where will He write them? ... *our minds* ...

Look at how He deals with our consciences in Hebrews 10:22:

. . .having our hearts sprinkled to ...*clense*............................ us from a ...*guilty*................. conscience. . .

As your mind begins to understand truth and you learn to live in it, it will set you free. Your conscience can remain clean, it can be brought alive, made acute and powerful again.

You may have heard truth before, but it was ineffective and your mind was full of lies. Now that you are in Christ, speaking truth to yourself will be effective. It will train you, it will formulate your thinking and it will set you free. Wonderful gospel! How exciting! It will actually affect your life!

Hebrews tells us that, under the old covenant, the blood of bulls and goats could never actually erase sin. It was a symbolic act. The people would watch the goats going off into the wilderness and they would know that that symbol of death to sin would mean their forgiveness for another year.

The problem was that it never actually got into their bloodstream, it never penetrated their minds to chase away evil in their thinking, it never touched their hearts or their consciences.

But Hebrews says of Jesus that His blood has touched our hearts and our consciences. It means my sin has actually been dealt with for ever, and that in my innermost being are springs of living water which can reach right into my mind to renew it and transform me.

You can have a renewed mind, you can have your impure thoughts, wrong motives, jealousies and fears dealt with by the Lord. This work of Jesus is all-powerful and able to deal with the enemy in all areas of your life – including and especially in your mind.

That has happened to you in Christ: light has invaded darkness, truth has invaded lies, your conscience has become acute and the veil has been removed to reveal understanding.

This is the state of your mind in Christ.

3. The Dynamics of Change

The crunch is this – it is not an instant process. That is not a depressing notion, but a releasing one for us. So many Christians live in a state of guilt about their minds based on this error; they believe their minds should have been instantly changed. They're some sort of second-rate, unholy Christian.

Understand this vital message: renewing the mind is a process of change. Write it out for emphasis.

Renewing the mind is ......**A PROCESS OF CHANGE**

(i) Destroying domination from the past

Many Christians are truly confused when they discover that despite being born again, baptized in water, baptized in the Spirit and all the other wonderful things of the Kingdom of God, they still are bugged by that same fear, phobia or problem that's been with them for years.

Have you noticed? You still have problems. God doesn't whisk you away from potentially fearful situations if you have a problem of fear. You don't discover endless daylight after you're saved if your problem is fear of the dark.

The Lord wants to teach you how to handle these situations with a renewed mind. When that is learnt there is a real and permanent victory for the gospel.

(ii) Taking every thought captive

We often come across Christians who have had deep-seated problems from the past, still reaching forward into their experiences today. Sometimes that person needs deliverance ministry. Such ministry can be very effective and very powerful in destroying the unwarranted clutches of the devil on a person's life. Our experience is often that, sadly, that sort of person falls back into similar difficulties.

What is the answer? More deliverance ministry? Was the first ministry unsuccessful then? No. We believe passionately that Jesus died to set the captive free, and He does. A person can be liberated in a moment, but what is necessary to *stay free* is a *renewed mind*. If a person learns to think according to the Word of God then that will enable them to stay clear and build fresh Godly ways where before they were open to the enemy re-dominating their mind.

25

Review

So, before we were in Christ, our minds were thinking futile thoughts, enemies of God, distorted in conscience and full of sin. Now, in Christ, we are totally forgiven, our conscience is liberated and we are being flooded with understanding and truth. A process of change has begun. It's a learning process, tapping into that new life within to bring about a renewing of our minds. What a great adventure lies ahead!

Chapter 3   WHO DO YOU THINK YOU ARE?

Before we get into the battle for the mind, that dynamic process of change which is open to you now you are saved, it is necessary to draw together all that we have touched on in the first two chapters about our background and what we are being renewed from.   Let us nail some issues.   Use this chapter to bring clarity, not condemnation!

The Effect of Our Upbringing

A major part of our background is, of course, how we were brought up. Look at Proverbs 22:6:

Train a child in the way he should go and ...*when he is and*
...*enough he will not turn from it*... .

This is the Word of God to parents and, as Christians, we want to work that through with our own children.

   Now do this exercise: rewrite the verse in the negative:

Train a child ...*in the way he should not go*...
...*and when he is old enough he will turn*... *not*   *from it*

Unfortunately, it is also true that if you have been trained in bad ways as a child, in wrong thinking and critical attitudes, you will find those ways as difficult to shake off as the areas you were well trained in.   It is much easier to stay with something you're used to rather than face up to a whole new way of thinking.

a)   Independence

A girl, saved a few years ago, had had a very difficult upbringing.   Her father had died when she was ten.   Her mother sat the children together after the funeral and asked them if they felt hurt.

"Yes," they all said, "it hurts a lot because Daddy has gone."

"Right," Mum replied, "and I am going to bring you up never to get close to anyone ever again so that you never have the possibility of facing this hurt again."

So she was brought up that way: never expressing herself emotionally, never letting herself get close or open up to anyone. She lived an isolated life, just considering herself. When she was born again and entered the Kingdom of God it was wonderful. Gloriously baptized in the Spirit and set free she went on tremendously for a few months.

Then the background began to reassert itself. Her background began to clash with the Word of God. Nowhere in the Word do you find God saying, "Be independent, live for yourself." In fact God says the very opposite – love one another, consider one another, open up your life to one another.

The way she got through was that she started to allow the Word of God to dominate her thinking. It was difficult at first, it took time, but gradually her ways were transformed by the renewing of her mind.

She had built walls round her life, she became a Christian and God smashed down the walls. Suddenly, she could see the horizon again! But her background reasserted itself: she felt exposed and in a dangerous place, so she started to rebuild the walls almost automatically. To stop and reverse that process she had to take the Word of God to her mind so that her past ceased to dominate her present.

b) Parental domination

Here is an area which often causes difficulties. Not least because the Word of God is clear that we should obey our parents as children and continue to honour them when we ourselves are in adulthood.

Often, however, we come across Christians who are under undue domination by their parents. They are not people in themselves, but puppets of their parents. This is a situation which can dominate, even as adults and even with Christian parents. Inevitably, there will be clashes with the Kingdom of God.

Turn to Matthew 10:37. What does it say should come first in your life?
Anyone who loves his father or mother more than me is not worthy of me (same person daughter).
This is difficult for us. We find that the sword that Jesus talks about a

28

couple of verses before (Matthew 10:34) is a painful thing sometimes. Yet it is to the end that we are free in our thinking and free to have a right and wholesome relationship with our parents.

c) Parental expectations

Another area of difficulty some of us have suffered is the persistent sense of failing to do as well as expected.

"Well, not bad, but . . . !"

"Second, huh! Well, you had it in you to come first, you know."

This is how teenagers find themselves hitting the valium to survive A levels – striving all the time to achieve, while inside they are dying through lack of love, support and compassion.

It needs to be rooted out of the mind. It is alien to the love and grace of God, and it is contrary to His attitude towards you.

d) Negativism

This, too, is often born out of bad attitudes from parents which are persistently drummed into us.

"You're useless, you're hopeless, you're as bad as your father!"

Sadly, so often we hear of upbringing where phrases like that rang round someone's mind year in, year out. It's devastating, and such an upbringing will continue to dominate your life until you let the truth of God's Word win the battle and reorientate your self-esteem.

e) Traumas

Sometimes you will discover people who have suffered dramatic or devastating events in their life which have dominated their response in certain situations. The memory keeps reverberating around their minds.

For example, many suffered traumatically as children in the war, and have abiding memories which seem somehow to carry their sting even into the new life in the Kingdom of God.

We could quote many other examples of trauma, particularly in childhood, but the point is this: God can heal you of the impact of those things on your life and your mind can be renewed so that your character is transformed into one unaffected by those events.

Here is a check list for you:

Upbringing: tick box if it affects you	
independence	✓
parental domination	☐
parental expectations	? ✓
negativism	✓
traumas	✓
other	✓

Present-day Pressures

The world in which we live is constantly trying to mould us into its way of thinking. There is daily pressure to be conformed to its attitudes and values. Just as we need to be renewed from our upbringing, so we need to be renewed from these unhealthy values which we have absorbed from the world. These things, too, become part of our background.

a) Materialism

Most Christians get into difficulties not because they have a lot of money to spend, but because of the way they think and their attitudes towards wealth. We could all use a lot more money if we had it, couldn't we? The issue is attitude, and attitudes reside in the mind.

The verse in the Bible most misquoted (by the world) is 1 Timothy 6:10. Write it out (the first part):

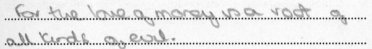

For the love of money is a root of all kinds of evil.

Now note it does not say *money* is a root of all kinds of evil, it says that it is the *love of money* that causes the problem. Materialism isn't a question of how much money you have, but a question of attitude. You can actually have hardly anything and still have problems of attitude. In fact, you can be quite poor yet be very materialistic in your outlook.

30

The Bible is radical, isn't it! Jesus said:

"You cannot ...serve......... both God and Money." (Matthew 6:24b)
The idea is that we serve the Lord and we receive whatever He provides.
But we don't live for money, we aren't motivated in our thinking and
therefore in our decision-making by the priorities of gaining wealth.

It's interesting how twisted and self-deceiving the world can be on this
subject. Look at your newspaper with the gossip columns and news often
gloating over the unhappiness and mess of the lives of the rich. Turn the
page and see the promotional offers: win this, win that, be happy!

b) Permissiveness
How easy it is to absorb the world's values in this area. Are Christians
simply following along behind at a discreet distance?

Many of us have been duped by sophisticated permissiveness on our
televisions. Soaps where immorality is dressed up in fancy language and
rich clothes are the norm. Does that make it acceptable? What life values
are being presented to you? It may be sophisticated, it may not be explicit,
but what is the philosophy you are absorbing as you watch? Try this test:
leave it for a year and then switch on again. It's just a different bed and
a different couple, but the same story line.

What about the "realistic" soaps? The nitty-gritty of life in all its raw-
edged detail. Bombarding you with "realism", but with what sort of
flavour? Do you need to be "entertained" by lives portraying the mess of
a Godless society?

These are the attitudes that dominate our society today. They are a
timebomb eroding everything, but especially the security and happiness of
Godly family life. As Christians we can still be letting our minds absorb
some of these values almost without noticing or caring until we discover
that we've lost out in the battle for the mind.

c) Passivity
This is becoming an increasing problem for us to face as Christians. It is
probably one of those national characteristics like cynicism which so
easily invade our lives. In these days of aggressive feminism it is particularly a problem for men.

We cop out, we back off, we try to stay as uninvolved as possible. It's a sort of defence mechanism. It's illustrated in the increasing portrayal of men in television comedy as wet wimps, dominated by the women in the story line. Perhaps you've noticed it's not just vicars who get this treatment these days!

It can saturate men's attitudes. We while away the hours, we while away the years and life goes by as we dissipate ourselves leaving the radical edge, the achievement in life, the goal-getting to others.

If that has even begun to enter your thinking, you need to be liberated and to have your mind renewed.

d) Fearfulness

Just as this can be a pressure from our upbringing so also it can be a pressure for us if we allow society's fears to infiltrate our Christian security in God.

People in our society today have an almost Pavlovian reaction to the news. Any disaster anywhere in the world will enter their thinking and dominate them with fear for their own future. You can list a few very easily by listening and observing: fear of the bomb, of radiation fallout from a reactor accident, of sickness epidemics, of contaminated food, of the greenhouse effect, of Libya, of Russia, of train crashes and bombs on aircraft – a world full of fear.

Some Christians allow themselves to live in fears like that, indistinguishable from the unregenerate who indeed has "no hope and is without God in the world". We need the truth of God to renew our minds, to liberate our thinking into the security He brings.

e) Media pressures

For most people the media have the function of doing your thinking for you. This is especially true of television. You switch off, they switch on – feeding you, instructing you, training you, convincing you. If your mind is not renewed you absorb the whole lot – hook, line and sinker. And you're sunk!

Of course the great cry of the opponents of Christianity is that you are moulded, you become narrow in your thinking. We need to refute that utterly. The reverse is true because the *media* are the greatest opportunity the world has for moulding attitudes, ideas and thinking. They have entry to your mind, and their philosophy – upfront or subtly behind the scenes – is humanism in various forms.

Ten years ago, presenting homosexuality as a valid alternative life style in schools was considered by an overwhelming majority of teachers to be wrong. Today the story is totally different. Have the issues changed? No? Then who has changed their minds? Opinion makers have won a battle for people's attitudes.

We need to be continually renewed from the pressures of the media. Adverts decide what's good-looking, what's in fashion; television decides ethics and feeds the theories of a Godless, evolutionary society in its documentaries. A recent parliamentary candidate was hounded by various pressure groups because his publicity shots included his wife and children – sexist anti-gay statement! These groups are so successful in moulding society's values that ordinary things like that can be vehemently condemned.

It has become the norm through television and newspaper bombardment. It is difficult to stand against the crowd. Let us recognize that peer pressure is enormous. It takes courage to say, even to yourself, "No! that is wrong."

We need to be renewed in our minds by the truth of God to stand clear on His principles whilst still remaining firmly part of our society. We don't want to be ascetics, withdrawing from contact with the world, but rather we want our lives to count as a proclamation of the Kingdom of God.

Now let us review these pressures we've looked at and see how far we have absorbed ungodly thinking into our minds. Be honest with yourself.

Present-day pressures: tick if they affect you	
materialism	☑
permissiveness	☑
passivity	☐
fearfulness	☐
media pressures	☑

PART TWO: THE BATTLEGROUND

Chapter 4 TAKING EVERY THOUGHT CAPTIVE

Now that we are convinced that renewing the mind is vital, we can press on to see how the Lord wants us to go about it. We have looked at the issues where our minds need to be renewed, and you can appreciate how impoverished your Christian life will be if there is no change in the area of your thinking.

We are going to look at the battleground and see that the Lord has provided us with suitable weapons. Using these weapons your life can be changed. We can become men and women who are victorious in the Kingdom of God.

Take Every Thought Captive
Look at 2 Corinthians 10:2-5:

Do we live by the standards of the world? .....no.............................

Do we live in the world? ....yes.................................

What sort of power is in our weapons? .....'divine power'.............

What do they demolish? .....strongholds & arguments.....
..........and pretension against knowledge of God........

What do we take as prisoners in the war? .....thoughts.............

What do we force our prisoners to do? .....make them obedient to God.....

When the Bible talks about strongholds, it is referring to the strongholds of the enemy. Until you were in Christ your mind was actually the territory of Satan and he ruled and reigned there whether you were aware of it or not. In fact he had such a field day there he built strongholds to consolidate his position.

Now that you have been born again Christ has authority, and far greater authority. You have been delivered from the kingdom of darkness and the rule of Satan into the Kingdom of God, where Jesus rules. There is authority there to pull down and destroy everything that Satan has built up over the years.

Who has final authority in your life? ....God..

What you have to realize is that Satan doesn't want to give up without a fight. There is a battle on. He has dominated your thinking and driven you along for years. He knows your weak spots, he knows where you have surrendered ground to him and he's built strongholds there.

Now look at it from the same perspective as Paul is doing in the passage in 2 Corinthians 10:5.

What sets itself up against the knowledge of God? ....

....arguments....and....pretensions...

The NASB version puts it this way: "speculations" and "lofty things". The clear implication is that these are baseless, arrogant lies. These things dominating you are not truth but arguments about truth and pretensions to truth. In the power of God they can be utterly destroyed. Praise God!

For example, if I come into a fearful situation, and that has been my weakness, and I begin to think fearful thoughts, it is because I have yet to take that thought captive and make it submit to the truth in Christ.

So Paul says we take *every* thought captive. There is land to be fought over in your mind – that's the battleground; let us make sure we are taking every thought that runs across that land prisoner. Catch them quick! Make them submit to the Lordship of Christ.

The Helmet of Salvation
Look at Ephesians 6:17:

Take the helmet of ....salvation..

Now this is interesting. When the Bible talks about salvation, it speaks of it in two contexts. One context is the salvation that is justification by faith; the other context is in the area of an outworking in life. It's a continual salvation – a "being saved" if you like.

You are continually being saved, but you are not being continually born again, again and again. Righteousness is a gift, it's the grace of God, you are justified and made right with God. It's yours. But the salvation process needs to go on and on in your life.

God wants to save you in your intellect and in your emotions now, as well as giving you a new body in the life to come. He is not "saving souls", He is saving people. Salvation needs to enter every part of your life.

When Paul talks about the helmet of salvation he is talking about your mind. Salvation needs to come to your thinking. Christians have been born again, but many struggle because salvation has not yet reached into their minds.

There are areas of your mind where Satan can land with impunity – landing strips, if you like, where the enemy zooms in and lands again and again. There was nothing there to guard your thinking or to bomb those landing strips, so in he comes.

We're walking along a road and we see something. Zoom! In comes the enemy and our thought life is in sin again. Or a situation arises and in he comes with another lie – zoom! He's landed, and it feels comfortable again because that's the way you always think.

We have to bomb these landing strips with the truth about our ongoing salvation in Christ. There have to be craters everywhere so that he cannot land! Take these landing strips captive for Christ!

Into Action!
Many Christians who do Bible study on the subject of the mind are surprised, as they dig into the scriptures, how many references there are to this subject in the New Testament. It is a major part of apostolic doctrine that we discipline our minds. Unfortunately you would be hard-pressed to find many people who speak on this subject regularly today.

Let us look at one of those verses – 1 Peter 1:13:

Prepare ..... you ..... mind ..... for ..... action .....

Be ..... self ..... controlled .....

What is the thrust of this verse? We're in a battle here; this is a battleground. Therefore be very positive – prepare your mind for action. Don't drift, says Peter, don't be casual. Gird up your minds, guard your minds, be sober in spirit and in your thinking be self-controlled.

Some Christians you look at have such potential, but somehow they never seem to accomplish what God has for them and they never really go anywhere in Christ. So often it is because they are laid-back sort of people. I'm sure you know the type. They tend to be casual, laid-back, friendly and fun. Actually, they are also casual in their thinking and laid-back about the battle in their minds – casual about whether or not they have their armour on and drifting about the battlefield with exposed heads!

Can you see that that is contrary to the scriptures? That is the root of their problem: their minds are not prepared for action.

Look at 1 Peter 5:8. The same message is there. Correct the deliberate mistakes in the following translation:

Be casual and sloppy. Your friend the devil wanders about like a purring lion looking for someone to lick.

This is not a game. Many of us fall in the area of the mind simply because we are lazy and ill-disciplined. We can't be bothered. You will be sniped at by the enemy and picked off if you have a casual approach to the way you think.

Recognize, too, that Satan is a liar and a deceiver. He won't jump out at you with horns and a spear and a big S on his T-shirt. You'd recognize him! He's also a deceiver so he disguises himself as something O.K. and reasonable.

For example, when you are tempted to think a wrong lustful thought, he lies to you. He says, "Come on, imagine! It'll give you a good time, it will satisfy you and you'll feel all the better for it."

Rubbish! We know it satisfies only for a moment and then comes condemnation. We know it doesn't fulfil us, but cuts us off from God and our walk with Him. Eventually, it devours and destroys us.

A lot of people blame the devil for their terrible days and weeks and persist in thinking they need deliverance. Actually they don't need deliverance, they need resistance. Resistance to that first thought, bomb that landing strip, make some craters around here!

"I'm so glad it's only the devil. We can deal with that straight away."

"But surely I need hours of ministry and deep, deep inner healing?"

37

"No, it's only the devil. No problem, he's only a liar and he's just conned you for a moment. Let's speak the truth about this."

"But I've booked myself out for three hours with you!"

"Well, you might need that to learn some scripture. Learn the truth, and speak it to your mind."

Your mind has been recaptured by Christ. He has the authority now. The devil has only one route left to get at you.

Write it in:

The devil can only ..*tempt*.. me.

Yes, he only has one weapon he can use on you in the battle for the mind. *Temptation*. Whether he is successful in that temptation or not is dependent upon how much room we give to temptation in our thinking. It is no good running to your homegroup leader or even your elders and pastors: "Please take my thoughts captive for me because I can't deal with them." They can't do it for you. You must do it for yourself.

Look up James 4:7:

Who do we submit ourselves to? ..*God*..

Whom do we resist? ..*the devil*..

What is the outcome? ..*he will flee from you*..

Simple, huh! It's a promise of God, there in the Bible in black and white. The promise isn't that he'll just slink away in a corner and sulk.

The promise is: he will ..*flee*.. from you.

He speeds off as fast as he can go. He disappears. He vanishes. His presence is no longer with you.

Remember, he's a liar. Start to see his words as lies and resist him. He has said to this nation: "Worship the god of sex. Give yourself to this god and you will be satisfied." But he doesn't tell the other side of the story. He doesn't tell of children's heartbreak as families split, he doesn't talk of thousands of ruined lives, of VD and AIDS, of abortion and the degradation of prostitution. The end result is misery: he is a liar and the father of lies.

Now use the following review to test what you have learnt in this chapter.

Review

1. How do we wage the war? What is the strategy? (2 Cor 10:3-5)

    Take every thought captive &
    make it obedient to Christ

2. What do we wear whilst we are engaged in the battle and why?
    (Eph 6:17) Helmet of Salvation
    ∴ minds protected from lies

3. How do we get ready for the battle? (1 Peter 1:13)

    Prepare our minds for
    action + being self controlled

Chapter 5 SUBSTITUTION

How Not to Succeed

Many Christians have a major misconception. They think that temptation is best defeated by concentrating on it. They believe that taking the thought captive to Christ requires intense concentrated effort.

For instance, you might have a lust problem. (If you are worried about anger, envy, fear etc., just delete lust and put in your word.) Having got thus far with this book, you feel ready to hit this. Your thinking goes something like this:

"Now, I've got to renew my mind, therefore I must get rid of this lustful thought. Lustful thought – I won't think it. Go away, lust! I rebuke you lust, I won't think of you lustful thought, I won't have you lustful thought, I stand against lust."

What has happened here? You have a person whose mind is dominated by the problem of lust. It's filling every moment. The enemy has trapped him into concentrating on his problem, not on the truth. Whole periods of time spent in futile battle with only one thing on his mind – lust!

Try this test out on a friend – preferably one who hasn't done this or heard of it before!

Stage 1: Sit still, close your eyes and think. Just think. Anything will do. Do that for a few moments.

Stage 2: Now tell your friend that whatever happens, under no circumstances must he or she think of white mice. It is strictly forbidden to think of white mice. Lay it on thick now; describe the white whiskers, the pink nose twitching, the long tail, but keep insisting to your friend that white mice must not be considered.

> **Stage 3:** Suddenly switch to grey elephants. Don't think about grey elephants. Lay it on as thick as before. Crashing through the undergrowth, huge trunks, big ears, look at those tusks! But under no circumstances think about grey elephants.
>
> **Stage 4:** What happened to the white mice?

This is the principle for winning the battle. You have a wrong thought. How are you going to deal with that wrong thought? *Fill your mind with right thoughts and the wrong thoughts go.* If I have a lust problem, I deliberately fill my mind with thoughts that are good, pure and right before God. With my mind dominated by truth, and understanding that these lustful thoughts are full of lies anyway and they won't do me any good, I find they simply bounce off me and are gone.

No Vacuum

A renewed mind does not just consist of ridding yourself of old thoughts. You need to replace those old thoughts with new ones. If we simply take the old thoughts captive we will be left with a vacuum. The enemy just loves vacuous people. Here is a very fertile ground for his temptations – a blank mind!

If you leave a vacuum the old thoughts will return again and again. This is a major cause of the ups and downs which many Christians suffer. I can rebuke the fearful thought, I can tell it Bible verses and I can see it flee, but if I don't replace it with fresh, Godly thinking I leave myself wide open to the return trip. Round it comes again, a fearful thought with its landing lights blazing looking for a nice bit of vacuous mind for a trouble-free touchdown.

The Scriptures

We need to exchange those thoughts taken captive to Christ with right thoughts. The Bible is very clear about that, too, as you will see from the following key references.

Look at Colossians 3:2:

set .... your minds on _things above_

not on ...... _earthly things_ ....

Turn to Philippians 4:8 and list the "whatevers" – there are eight of them:

true, pure, holy, lovely, admirable,
are noble, excellent or praiseworthy

What are we to do with these things? ....

Back to Colossians 3:16. Fill in the missing words:

Let the word of Christ ...... _dwell_ ...... in you ...... _richly_ ......

Now look at Colossians 2:6-7:

... continue to live in him, ... _rooted_ ...... and ...... _built up_ ......

in him . . .

Successful substitution comes from being rooted and grounded in Christ's word, having a new mind set, dwelling on Godly things in a positive way. Encourage yourself into biblical thought patterns. If your mind is full of the truth of God there's no room for the enemy to land. He comes in with his lies, landing lights on to attract attention, but he simply has to do a circuit and fly back to where he came from. That is the result of a mind set on things above, dwelling on the truth.

Ceaseless Traffic

We need to recognize that ungodly thoughts have ploughed through our minds in a ceaseless traffic for years. Attitudes and habitual reactions have formed a cavalcade of unrighteous thinking. Illustrated like that, we begin to see how deeply ingrained these thoughts have been.

We have all seen those deeply rutted farm tracks, haven't we? Day in, day out, in all weathers, for years and years the farmer has taken his tractor and trailer and his Range Rover up and down the track. Up and down, up and down. The result is two deep ruts worn firmly (or muddily!) into the ground clearly defining the wheelbase of his vehicles. The ruts are usually marked by tractor tyres and they're usually rough and bumpy, with a high ridge of grass separating them.

Similarly, your mind has been scored by the ceaseless traffic of ungodly thinking. Your mind is used to it. In fact, it even begins to feel right. It begins to feel comfortable as the enemy cruises down the well-worn ruts in his Range Rover marked ''temptation''. It feels natural to be full of fear, it feels comfortable to be indulging self-pity, and someone only has to make a quick remark and we're off, down the track again.

Now when you become a Christian it's as if you are given a new car. Here you are in your brand new mini of Godly thoughts. Very pleased, you drive swiftly into your mind only to find that the way forward is very uncomfortable. Your mini doesn't fit the ruts! At best you'll bump along at first, you might even get stuck on the grass ridge, wheels spinning!

Is that your experience? Godly thoughts ride uneasily in your mind. They even appear alien to its environment.

The solution is not to throw away the car, but to drive up and down the tracks of your mind incessantly in your Godly thoughts vehicle. You now need a cavalcade of Godly thoughts – up and down, up and down. You need to do this continuously to create new ruts of thinking in your mind. New tracks that will bias your mind towards righteousness, a new environment in your attitudes, so that it becomes the ungodly thoughts which are out of place and uncomfortable in the new righteous ruts of your mind. Those old wheels won't fit the new course on which you are set, they're in for a rough ride!

Know the Right Thoughts

''Fine,'' you say, ''I'm with you thus far, that's a great illustration, but I don't know what are the right thoughts. I don't know the truth to apply in these situations.''

For many of us, brought up in very legalistic situations, it was one of the great eye-openers of the charismatic movement that God, in His grace, was not watching over us with a big stick to make sure we read our Bibles every morning between 6 and 6.30 a.m.

What liberty! What release! We discovered the heavens didn't fall in if we didn't manage to read anything for a whole week. Then a month, then a year! What liberty! Until, one day, you discover that the issue isn't Bible reading actually, but knowing what the Word of God says. We discover that we need to be soaking ourselves in the scriptures, taking every opportunity to read what God says in His Word.

If we do not know the word of truth how are we going to counteract lies? If we have not got a ready armoury of the truth of God we are not even going to go into the battle, let alone win it. If we are not saturating ourselves in truth, how are we going to create mind-changing cavalcades of it?

The Bible isn't a passive book, it's not just words on a page. It's God speaking to me, it's truth that will penetrate my heart and mind. It will change me. It is not a case of having to read the Bible every day, the issue is this: when you realize you can't live without the Word of God, you can't get enough of it. Each day there are battles to be fought and battles which will be won if the truth of God dwells in me.

Agree with God

We need to agree with the things God says about ourselves. You need to know His attitude towards you and how He sees you, rather than how you see yourself.

Stop agreeing with your pessimistic, cynical, passive self and start agreeing with God and His vibrant, glorious, certain, secure view of who you are in Him. Our minds should be filled with His ability, His power, His authority, His determination to see us changed.

Look at 2 Corinthians 3:18:

What is happening to us? We are being transformed

Whose likeness? the Lord's

Whose power is achieving this? Holy Spirit

Obviously, there is not space here to quote suitable scripture verses for every fear, phobia or temptation. In any case we need to be very familiar, not just with particular verses, but with the great themes of our relationship with God which run through the scriptures. We can look at some examples, though, to give you the flavour of how to approach things.

Fears

Suppose you are afraid of the dark. Many people are, and often it first begins with a traumatic experience in childhood. You can have ministry for that, you can be delivered from the stronghold of Satan which he has built up on the back of that experience, but what you need for continuing

44

in victory is the Word of God. It needs to be saturating your mind. Now comes the moment! You are alone in the house one evening, clearing up. You have to go out to the dustbin – in the dark! But here comes the Word of God – read Psalm 91:1-7:

You ...*will not*... the terror of the night . . . (v5)

Nor ...*the pestilence*... that stalks in the darkness . . . (v6)

Matthew 28:20b:

"And surely ...*I will be with you*... ,

to ...*the ends of the earth*... ."

Romans 8:38-39 – sum up the phrases with one word:

N ...*OTHING*... will be able to separate us from the love of God. We must decide: either these were nice thoughts and pleasant poetry written many centuries ago or they are the Word of God that will pierce you and fill you and make you more than conquerors. They are full of the power of God even today.

Phobias

Maybe you have a phobia about flying. If you have been to Guernsey on the unpressurized, low-flying "vomit-comet" I can understand it! I have experienced it. We began our trip looking like humans, and after half an hour of bouncing around the sky we all looked like Martians. Suddenly, for the first time in countless flights, I was frightened.

Afterwards there were more flights. Off to the USA, for instance, in a great big, beautiful, super-smooth 747. Up at 30,000 feet the fear came again. Then the recall of all those films: Airport 77, 78, 79 – then they ran out of numbers – planes with dead pilots, planes under the water, and planes without wings. The series became ridiculous in the end. But I remembered and fear gripped me. I sat sweating, panicky and wretched.

Decision time. Either this happens every time I fly – and I've got to get back home the same way – or I renew my mind and fill it with God's word. John 16:33, for example:

45

"I have told you these things so that ..... *in me you may have peace*

In this world you will have trouble. But ..... *take heat*
.................................! I have ..... *OVERCOME the world*."

"Wonderful! You have overcome the world, Lord, that means You're in control here. My life isn't in the enemy's hands, it's in God's hands."
Philippians 1:21 is also very relevant here:

For to me, to live ..... *is Christ* ....

and to die ..... *is gain* ....

"Great, if the plane goes down I'm O.K., in fact it'll be even better for me. I'm at peace with my Lord. Hey! this journey is quite pleasant after all. Pass the steak."

Under Pressure

Some years ago I was very ill. The doctors couldn't find anything wrong. Tests followed more tests, but all were inconclusive. I was out of action for about a year with this unknown illness. I felt low, I felt that no one understood me and I felt isolated. Fertile ground for the enemy. My mind could have been wide open, with landing strips the width of three motorways. But I began to fill my mind with the Word of God. Yes, I'm weak and weary, but here is the promise for me, in Isaiah 40:29-31:

". . . those who hope in the Lord ..... *WILL* ..... renew their strength . . . ."
I read and reread that passage to ensure it was firmly in my mind, creating new Godly statements about myself. Whatever state I was in, whatever my day was like – good, bad or indifferent – I fed and drank off that passage. I am not ashamed to say I took it as my medicine three times a day after meals!

Encouragement of the Word

Be ready to encourage yourself with the Word of God. Go further than that, be ready to speak out to others relevant scriptures for their situations. Minister to others what you minister to yourself.

This doesn't have to be intense and super-spiritual. You don't have to be a kind of biblical robot walking around quoting verses at everything and everyone. People like that are simply living in unreality. You don't have to be like those actors who play Jesus in the films, gazing with glazed, super-holy expressions into camera 3 whilst speaking in a slow, deep, sonorous voice.

When people say:

– "I can't", say, "Look, the Word of God says you can do all things through Christ who will strengthen you."

– "I'm defeated." Say: "God always leads us in triumph through Christ."

– "I'm scared of the devil." No: "Greater is he that is in you than he who is in the world."

– "God doesn't love me." What! "There is therefore now *no* condemnation for those in Christ Jesus."

Confess the Word of God to yourself and to each other.

This is not the power of positive thinking, or mind over matter. It is simply ensuring that the Word of God becomes part of your thinking, making new tracks in your mind, and giving the enemy a really rough time.

When we want to know about our weaponry in spiritual warfare we naturally turn to Ephesians 6.

Look at Ephesians 6:10-17. One of the pieces of equipment mentioned there is for offensive use, the rest are defensive.

Which is it? ..... *Sword of the Spirit*

That's the biblical analogy. Look again at verse 17.

What does this sword consist of? ..... *the Word of God*

Now isn't that interesting? Just what we have been looking at in the last chapter. The sword is a weapon of war. It's used to attack the enemy. The Bible is very clear on this point: we attack the enemy with the Word of God. Jesus did it in the wilderness. The Word of God was already filling His mind ready to be brought swiftly and appropriately into play.

The sword cuts straight through, no messing about (although the results on the enemy can be very messy indeed!). It's not for display purposes, to be hung on a wall and gazed at. No, it's for action. It enables us to go on the offensive. The Word of God is our weaponry to pull down strongholds, to cut away the lies of the enemy, to renew our thinking and to guard our minds from further attack.

Hebrews 4:12 says that the Word of God is living and active, sharper than any double-edged sword. Let us look at the two edges of this sword of the Word, which will be effective in renewing the mind. The first, which we will deal with in this chapter, is that the sword gets to the root of the problem, cuts it out and sorts you out. The second, the subject of Chapter 7, is that the sword exposes the enemy and thrusts him through. (Ugh! The battle for the mind is not for the squeamish!)

Exposing the Root

Look up Hebrews 4:12 again. Read it through.

That describes a pretty lethal weapon. It pushes right through to the thoughts and the attitudes of the heart. That's radical.

If we're honest, many Christians don't see the Word of God like that at all. They find it boring, irrelevant and often dull, and they don't realize that actually it is awesome, and that it reveals mercilessly the intentions of people's hearts.

Often, when trying to help others, we are in problems because, firstly we don't know the Word of God well enough, secondly we are not practised at using what we do know, and thirdly we are scared of upsetting people. We want to be nice and understanding, cosy and chatty. We don't like upsetting people and we want to be popular.

Having a chat, waffling on, even having a bit of a debate about an issue doesn't get to the root and deal with it. The Word of God, correctly applied, will expose the root. It can be painful and distressing sometimes and it certainly won't leave you untouched, but it is supremely effective in dealing with your motives.

How many prophesies do you hear? How many can you remember? You remember the ones that spoke the Word of God to you, that cut through to roots, that caused change in your life. Sometimes you can't remember them from a week ago, but you can remember ones that really spoke to you years back. That's the power of the Word of God that flowed in them. Scripture is even more powerful.

Four Root Problems

Four particular areas of attitude in the heart are common to people who are in difficulties in their minds: passivity, pride, lack of faith and lack of devotion.

1. Passivity

This is a heart attitude that can dominate the mind, making us lethargic and slow to respond, unable and unwilling to stir ourselves. As a result we constantly fail to hit targets and meet goals in our lives.

Often it is exacerbated by overfamiliarity. If you are overfamiliar with the Word of God your attitude will be: I've heard it all before, I know that.

As a result, the Word bounces off you. It never penetrates into you because it hits a wall, a wall of passivity, and simply bounces off again. People with this problem of passivity are apathetic and lazy, unprepared to stir themselves and sharpen their thinking.

Read Proverbs 24:30-34:

What are the three things observed in the sluggard's field?

thorns

weeds

stone wall in ruins

What is the heart attitude of the sluggard in verse 33?

apathy

What is the result in verse 34?

poverty & scarcity

Can you sum up this result in one four-letter word? R.*UIN*

No wonder the enemy tries to make it as difficult as possible for us to spend time meditating on God's word. It is a problem nearly all Christians face at some time or other. We pick up our Bibles and immediately we can think of four or five different things that are suddenly pressing matters that need to be dealt with at once. Sometimes we would even rather attend to the washing up!

Then, when we have settled down to it, we have difficulty concentrating. There's a battle on. We become sleepy and inattentive, we read a passage and nothing goes in. Our eyes have slid over the words and our minds have let the meaning of them slip by like a dream. We have become dulled and overfamiliar. We know that these words can come to life, we know that fresh insight and faith-stirring revelation can come from the most well-worn pages of our Bibles, but through a passive heart attitude the enemy steals away the potential for fruitfulness.

Passivity seems to be a particularly ingrained problem for British people and it becomes so for British Christians, too. It is really only in recent years that we have regained any sense of purpose as a nation. In primary schools in the fifties you would see maps of the world on the wall covered in pink – the colour of the British Empire.

Since then we have cut back, and cut back, been the laughing stock of other nations, suffered the "British disease" at work and hooliganism at play. It has been retreat, retreat. The map now has a little blob of pink in the North Sea, and three tiny blobs, one at the tip of Spain, one at the tip of Argentina, and one at the tip of China.

That spirit has fed into the way we think, the way we live life, and has closed us up as a nation. We lack creativity and vibrancy, we lack pioneering spirit, we have become inward-looking and closed up as people.

The problem in most people's lives is apathy, despite the "yuppie" minority. Look at your neighbours for evidence. Many will have stopped living and now just exist in a day-to-day humdrum. Ask yourself the question: how much of that passive, apathetic attitude have I taken on board?

List some areas of your life where you know you are predominantly passive and find it difficult to be decisive. Here are two suggestions to get you started: tick them if they apply to you.

Disciplining yourself to regular Bible study ✔

Sorting out arguments between the children

Tidiness ✓

household chores ✓

organisation ✓

Christian living is supposed to be a life full of adventure. How, then, can we be passive *and* successful in our lives? So often we see Christians with all the potential and all the gifting, but they are passive and lazy. They don't have a sense of personal responsibility and accountability for what they hear. The result is that the Word of God does not penetrate their life and their thinking.

Look at Luke 12:48, and the second sentence:

"From everyone who has been given much, *much will be demanded*;

and from the one who has been entrusted with much, *much more will be asked* "

We are so fortunate to have access to so much teaching, to so many books and tapes and so on. We say that we're pioneers, we're moving on in God, but the word to the passive is: just how true is that of you? Don't let's kid ourselves.

When we come before Him and He says: "What about your family – it was such a mess," you will not be able to reply that no one was available to advise you at the time. Most telling of all, you will not be able to say you didn't have the Word of God. You can see films and videos, read books and listen to tapes, you can go to seminars and hear it on Sunday, but the issue is: has the Word of God penetrated your life?

Remember our verse, Luke 12:48? The converse must also be true. Five little old ladies sitting faithfully in the pews of a chapel somewhere and only hearing liberal theology every Sunday will not have much required of them. That's radical, isn't it? We are responsible for what we hear and there is no room for passivity.

Jesus had a favourite phrase. Write out Matthew 13:9:

"He *who has ears let him hear* "

Every time you hear the Word proclaimed or study the scriptures, ask the Lord to cause it to penetrate. Say to yourself, "I want this to penetrate, I'm responsible for what I'm hearing and reading and I want to do something about it." We can have churches full of hearers who are only half-listening, but it is those who "hear" with every fibre of their body, and who are "doers" of the Word, who are the ones actually receiving it.

Deliberately shrug off passivity and laziness. When the word on Sunday is about a familiar subject, refuse that thinking which says, "I've heard it all before, I know this already." Actively seek more from it, have an attitude and a posture which speaks of your desire to receive fresh impetus in your life even in the familiar areas.

Remind yourself of the parable of the sower (Matthew 13:1-9) and tick the box with the correct answer:

Is the story about the seed? ☐

or the soil? ☑

The parable is focusing on *receptivity*. It's the state of the *soil* which counts. The seed is the same wherever it lands. Good soil is the lives of people who are able to receive again and again. The density of the crop is dependent on the receptivity of the soil.

2. Pride

Pride is another heart attitude which will really mess up your mind. The Word of God says in 1 Peter 5:5:

Clothe yourselves with ...*humility*... ....*towards*.............................. one another . . .

We need this attitude in us because we will be hearing the Word of God again and again. In order to receive it and see it begin to change me and renew my mind, I am going to need humility.

Teaching people who are proud is impossible. There are three main reasons:

(i) Proud people come with *preconceived ideas*. It means that they have formed an opinion or an idea of what they believe beforehand. Speaking to them is pointless because their minds are made up.

(ii) Proud people are *presumptuous*. They presume that their understanding is correct. They already know the truth of the matter. They can handle this, there is nothing you can teach them they don't already know, and, what's more, have more experience of than you.

(iii) Proud people *don't listen*. Either they switch off in a self-righteous cloud of smugness, barely aware of what is being said. Or they sit on the edge of their seat waiting to pounce on the first "mistake", prejudging the course of the word and often 'hearing' things that haven't been said.

Do you know people like that? That's easy, we all seem to know someone like that, the more important question is: do you recognize yourself here?

Honestly tick the boxes below. The exercise will do you good!

	Preconceived ideas	Presumption	Don't listen
Nearly always	☐	☑	☐
Frequently	☑	☐	☐
Fairly often	☐	☐	☐
Sometimes	☐	☐	☑
Hardly ever	☐	☐	☐

Be clothed with humility, be receptive, be good soil whether listening to preaching or reading the Word.

In Proverbs there is an often repeated phrase which is translated in the AV "incline thine ear". In the NIV the translation of that phrase is most often "pay attention". The couplet to it usually says something like "apply your heart". To see examples of this look at Proverbs 2:2, 4:20, 5:1 and 22:17.

Here is an exercise for you: try to incline your ear *without* moving your head! Some of us can twitch our ears up and down, but to incline our ears actually requires us to bow our heads. We have to make a movement which, in effect, is an attitude of submission and an acknowledgement of the superior.

So these verses are saying something very profound; they're saying that we need to have a heart attitude of humility to be able to hear properly.

We have two options when we read the Word. We can either let the familiar words slip easily across the mind – the pleasing poetry, the easy phrase with the nice ring to it – or we can sit down and get stuck in, taking it phrase by phrase and applying it to ourselves.

3. Lack of faith

Look at Hebrews 4:2:

The message the Israelites heard was of no value to them because:

they did not combine it with faith

We can listen to the Word, we can be intent on it, but it will remain just words to us if our heart attitude is not one of faith. Without faith in the Word, it will not be fruitful in us. We must mix what we hear with faith, otherwise it remains ineffective.

For example, we can hear about signs and wonders at a conference, but it will be just notes in my notebook, words on a tape and jargon in a book unless my heart attitude is to believe it. We must be ready to receive it as truth, to let it penetrate our thinking, to let it be tied in and twinned with faith. Otherwise all that will remain will be dry verses unrelated to life, and the opportunities will have been lost.

4. Lack of devotion

Here is a fourth heart attitude which can be a root problem. A lack of devotion forms a barrier to the presentation of the Word of God.

Look at Acts 2:42:

They ......*devoted*........ themselves to the ......*apostles*......
......*teaching*...... and to the ......*breaking fellowship*......, to the
......*breaking of bread*...... and to ......*prayer*...... .

When the Word of God comes to you, it may break through *passivity* and *pride*, and it may break through your *lack of faith*, because you are beginning to build that into your life, but there is often this final barrier of a *lack of devotion*. One verse spoke of the devotion of those first Christians. They devoted themselves "continually" is the emphasis of the NASB translation.

We need to give ourselves utterly to that which God is speaking to us about. For example, if it is a lack of faith then I will give myself to the pursuit of faith. I will read books, listen to tapes, and I will put myself alongside people of faith and drain them dry of everything they know, following their example. I am on a mission to get faith into my life.

With this attitude we will not be content to float and drift through life. It will not be enough to say: "Yes, I'm thinking about faith, I'm meditating on it a little bit." No, we must devote ourselves to the Word of God.

Look at 1 Thessalonians 5:6:

What mustn't we be, like others? ......*asleep*......

What must we be? ..... *alert + self-controlled*

Turn to 1 Timothy 4:15:

What does Paul ask Timothy to be? ..... *diligent* .....

What is to be his attitude? ..... *giving himself wholly* .....

What will everyone see, as a result? ..... *his progress* .....

Look at it this way: life is too short to let it drift by and to waste it on passivity, pride, lack of faith and lack of devotion. The Word of God is a sword. It is a weapon of attack. First, let it attack you. Let it cut into you and expose those layers of bad attitudes in your heart.

Prayers of Commitment

Passivity

"Father, through Your grace and the power of Your Spirit, I will shrug off passivity. I will be alert, I will be responsible for everything I hear. I determine not to be a sluggard, but one who seeks the penetration of the Word of God to lead me into action."

Pride

"Father, I recognize my need to clothe myself with humility. I desire to be good soil out of which will come a harvest of change in my mind. I determine to listen with an open heart, always ready to hear again and again. I put down my preconceived ideas; I just want Your truth to change me."

Lack of faith

"Yes, Lord, You've sent Your Word out to accomplish things. It is there to bear fruit in my life, to be mixed with faith. I proclaim that it is not a word simply for centuries gone by, but that it is powerfully effective now, today, in my life. It can and will change me from one degree of glory to another."

Lack of devotion

"I recognize, Father, my drift and lack of commitment. I know it has delayed and damaged me. I want to be diligent to pursue everything You speak to me about. I know You only speak to me with purpose, that I might be more victorious in my thinking and in my life. I want to grasp hold of that for which You took hold of me, and I recognize it needs my heart to be devoted to Your Word and Your purposes."

Remember, we are now pitched into the centre of the battle for the mind. We have seen how God's Word is a sword which can pierce through and deal with our own heart attitudes.   If they are not dealt with they will trip us up and cause us to suffer defeats in the battle.

The sword is also an offensive weapon for attacking the enemy.   It can be wielded by us to refute the lies of Satan.   Remember that we saw the issue was not just avoiding wrong thoughts, but replacing those wrong thoughts with the Word of God and what He says about us.

If we are saturated in the Word of God, if it has been penetrating our thinking and our mind has been trained to be set on the things of the Spirit, then Satan has a problem!   As he comes in to do battle and try to reclaim the ground he has lost, ground that was once under his control, he finds instead the Word of God like a sword flashing out at him.   In every direction he turns he will see row upon row of swords ready to run him through!

The sword of the Word of God is in your mind.   It is an offensive weapon set to attack and ready to penetrate the lies of the enemy and expose him for what he is.   The enemy has been dethroned, and now we have the mind of Christ.   He has no hold over us, we have died to ourselves and our lives are hidden with Christ in God. That is wonderful, but the enemy will come back at us again and again with his one weapon.   Let us spend some time learning about this one and only weapon: *temptation*.

How Temptation Operates

From over the horizon
The enemy doesn't own any camps in your mind.   He has been ousted by Jesus.   You have been placed by God "in Him".   Look at Ephesians 1:4-14.   There are four "in Him"s in that passage that remind us that we have

been transferred from one kingdom to another.   Fill them in:

Eph 1:4   Chosen *in Him* before the creation of the world
               to be *holy + blameless in his sight*

Eph 1:7   Redemption and forgiveness *in Him* in accordance with
               the riches of God's grace

Eph 1:11-12   Chosen *in Him* and predestined by His will in order that
               we might be for the praise of his glory

Eph 1:13   Included in Christ and sealed *in Him* by *the Holy Spirit*

We haven't been left to drift, we have been placed in Him. We are
protected by Him and empowered by the Holy Spirit. The devil doesn't
have any rights or authority over you or your thinking. He doesn't reign
any more; he's out there with his solitary weapon hoping to fly in over the
horizon, under your radar, and catch you off guard with his lies.

Sortie objectives
As he flies in, he has one weapon and one objective: to take back ground
he has lost. He wants to use temptation to re-establish a bridgehead into
your mind. He wants to get back his grip on some corner of your mind.

The landing place
Temptation is the weapon Satan uses, if you like, as he hovers over your
thinking.   Temptation is not some external stimulus which grabs your
attention, temptation is a thought in your mind. It is Satan's point of entry,
and if he is having a heyday in our thinking it is because we haven't yet
learned how to deal with tempting thoughts.   There are areas of our mind
where the sword of the Word is not pointing menacingly at the enemy,
ready to repulse any salvo of temptation.

The end result

The end result that Satan is looking for is that you might be enticed into sin. He may start by speaking just a little thought and lying to you that if you dwell on it it will be satisfying, relieve the pressure, give you a thrill inside – or whatever – but his end result will be sin in your life.

Look at James 1:14-15:

Who does the enticing? ....the Devil..

From what are you dragged away? ....God..

Fill in the progression:

temptation ⟶ d esire ⟶ s in ⟶ d eath

In these verses we see that James, like Paul in Romans 6:11-12, has a radical but biblical view of Christian living which is not very common these days: you don't have to sin! In fact the normal Christian life is to walk with God; sin should be an interruption, not a regular occurrence.

Turn to 1 John 1:9:

If we confess our sins He is ....faithful................ and .....just. and ...will forgive us our sins and cleanse us from all unrighteousness.

The word is clear: you will always be able to go to the throne of grace and receive total, utter forgiveness. The problem is that many people live defeated lives. They seem to be on a continuous cycle: sin, confession, forgiveness, sin; round and round. We have a forgiving God and He will forgive and forgive. The sacrifice Jesus made will always be sufficient to atone for every sin. But the devil has got a foothold, a landing strip, a corner of your mind with ready access for him to be successful with his one weapon of temptation.

God wants us to live and walk with Him continually. The enemy knows that and his objective is to keep interrupting that as often and as regularly as he can. He does that by enticing us to sin as often as he can. In that way he can keep us immature, he can keep us condemned and ineffective and he can draw us away from the fullness of what God wants for us.

60

The Characteristics of Temptation

Having seen how the enemy deploys his weaponry, let us spend a little time having a closer look at the weapon itself. This is very important because it will help you to be more accurate with your sword!

Temptation is nice

There is no point in the devil tempting us with thoughts and ideas that we find obnoxious or revolting. We wouldn't fall for it, would we? It is amazing how many people overlook this simple fact and its implications. What is presented to you must have some attraction to you at some level or another. Often it is seemingly true and it has the appearance of being accepted. Often it accentuates the pleasure and fails to remind you of the penalties and the misery that will follow. Satan is a liar and a schemer. The Bible acknowledges this.

Look at Hebrews 11:25:

Moses joined the Israelites rather than ..... *enjoy the pleasures of sin for a short time* .....

If everyone were to receive 100 volts of electricity every time we were tempted we wouldn't enjoy the process much. Not many of us would run to embrace the prospect. Satan knows that, so temptation comes with a smile and an enticement. To try to identify it by whether it feels all right will be a very unreliable indicator. Rather we need to recognize it by comparison with the Word of God.

Look at Luke 4: 1-4. Here is an example of temptation in action.

How was Jesus feeling? ..... *hungry* .....

What was Satan offering? ..... *food* .....

Was that an attractive proposition

in the short term?	Yes ☑	No ☐
in the long term?	Yes ☐	No ☑

Temptation is not sin

Here is another radical, but true fact about the devil's weapon which we must understand for successful warfare. To suffer temptation, to have that first thought invade your mind, is not the same thing as committing sin.

Some Christians find themselves in all sorts of turmoil because they are tempted. Yet if we look at Hebrews we find very clear statements about the life Jesus led and how He, too, was tempted. We remember that Jesus was tempted in the wilderness after his baptism in a special way, but we often forget that He was tempted in *every* area of life. It is crucial for us to understand this.

Turn to Hebrews 4:15 and fill in the second phrase of the verse:

... we have one (Jesus) who *was tempted in every way, just as we are - yet was without sin*

Jesus knows all about your temptations. He lived through life bombarded by the enemy's lies and guile, yet He lived through it without giving in once to those temptations. He accomplished what Adam failed to do – a life without sin – so that He became that second victorious Adam in the fight.

Look at Hebrews 2:18:

Was Jesus tempted? Yes ✓ No ☐

How did He feel when tempted? *he suffered*

Temptations didn't bounce off Jesus without Him noticing. They were not like water off a duck's back to Him. He, too, had to "suffer" the process of recognizing, determining and dealing with temptation. He, too, had to suffer the antagonism of the enemy as he tried to break down godliness and righteousness wherever he saw it.

We need to recognize that, at the point of thinking that thought, nothing has happened. For instance, suppose you are on a diet. You are walking along the High Street and the thought of eating a chocolate eclair comes into your mind. The picture in my mind is clear: cream oozing out and thick, dark chocolate on top, and your mind reminds you of that delicious taste.

That is temptation. But if I dwell on that idea, if I run the thought round and round in my mind, if I begin to salivate, I'm in problems. I will begin to decry my diet and make excuses to myself as to why it would be O.K. to enjoy just one eclair.

In no time at all, I find my steps taking me, as if by magic, to the cake shop. Somehow I'm inside, and somehow, strangely, as if it's someone else, I find myself asking the girl behind the counter for eclairs. Lo and verily! In two minutes all that is left to remind me of eclairs are:

Exhibit A – an empty paper bag smudged with chocolate

Exhibit B – a sticky mouth surreptitiously wiped by the back of my hand

Exhibit C – a guilty conscience.

That is succumbing to temptation, letting it dominate my thinking and turn me to sin. Inevitably the sin bore fruit in sinful action. But, remember, the first thought was not sin, it was *temptation*. And, what is more, *temptation that could have been dealt with*.

Temptation never goes away

Another point we need to understand about temptation is that it never goes away. If you think that one day you will be living the perfect life and Satan will sink away into the background, you are very mistaken. There is no such thing as a temptationless state.

Some people think that Jesus, after being tempted by Satan in the wilderness, then went through the rest of his life in a sort of holy haze. Yet as we study the Bible we see that He continually faced temptations. The enemy came back again and again.

In fact, as we look at the garden of Gethsemane, we find there that Jesus went through a very real and substantial battle with temptation. There was a battle on in the mind. As His ministry reached its climax, as the cross and its agonies loomed ahead, so Jesus fought against the temptation to turn back from God's purposes.

Luke's account is very graphic. Read Luke 22:39-46, and note especially verses 40, 42 and 46.

What temptations do you think lay ahead for these disciples in the days to come?

renouncing Jesus
+ taking the easy way out

We are not going to be rid of temptation. Its intensity will vary perhaps.

Sometimes it will be very strong, particularly if we are foolish and place ourselves in its path. Sometimes we may not be too troubled by it, especially if we have shown consistent strength in an area. What is sure, though, is that we must be always alert and ready, for Satan will never give up trying to destroy the life God has brought to you.

Look at some examples of this alertness and note the means Satan uses to tempt you to stumble in your Christian walk.

2 Corinthians 2:10-11 .... *forgiving others*

1 Timothy 3:7 .... *good reputation with outsiders*

2 Peter 3:17 .... *be on your guard*

Galatians 6:1 .... *watch yourself*

There is never room for complacency in this area of temptation. Some young people think that it will all ease off when they are older. A picture is painted of an increasingly relaxed life as we get older. This is unwittingly reinforced by the way we often hear older people talk about the pressures on the younger generation. They look with horror, wondering how Christian young people survive, readily commenting that it was a lot easier in their day.

This is nonsense. We do not slide in the cruise control as we pass into middle age. Temptation continues. The form it takes may vary, may be more subtle and less blatant in some areas, but it continues.

Look at 1 Corinthians 10:12.

So, if you think you are .... *standing tall*

be careful that you don't .... *fall*

Temptation will be with us for life. Isn't that good news! Temptation is here to stay, so the issue is: what are you going to do about it?

How to Counterattack

We've seen how temptation operates, and we've noted two important facts – that temptation in itself is not sin, and that temptation will always be with us as the enemy's only weapon.

Now it's time to go on the counterattack, to move into the offensive. The best form of defence is attack! We have accumulated knowledge about the ways in which the enemy attacks and the capabilities of his weapon. Now we can begin to build our counteroffensive.

The second thought

Here is a key verse which will direct us to the initial manoeuvre of the counterattack. Let's look at the first part of it.

Look at 1 Corinthians 10:13. Read the first sentence:

No temptation has seized you except ...*what is common to man*

Sometimes we feel we are in a particularly hopeless position. We feel that no one could possibly have been tempted in quite the same way as us or with such intensity as we experience. Often people will say things like, "But you don't know me," or "I'm sure no one else is really tempted like me."

It really is a combination of self-pity and arrogance. Who do you think you are anyway! Unique in the whole human race?! No, of course not. Actually many people are being similarly tempted throughout the world every day.

Now read the second sentence of 1 Corinthians 10:13:

And God is faithful ...*he will not let you be tempted beyond what you bear*

The grace of God to us is marvellous, isn't it? There is no temptation beyond your bearing. That's good news, but it leaves us without excuse!

We cannot say, "It's hopeless, I just can't cope." We cannot duck out with a lame, "It just overwhelms me." This is the truth of God's Word to you and me today – you can resist!

The third sentence of the verse gives us our opportunity for counterattack. Read the last part of 1 Corinthians 10:13:

But when you are tempted, he will ...*provide a way out so that you can stand up under it*

With every temptation there's a way of escape. A way out so that you can stand. That's the promise of God to us. There will always be such a way. It doesn't say "sometimes" or even "frequently", but it says God will *always* provide a way of escape.

How do we recognize it? If we're to side-step that attack from Satan and start our counteroffensive we must be alert to the opportunity.

My experience is this. Hard on the heels of that first thought – the temptation – comes a second. Almost inseparable, running alongside it, if you like, comes the second thought. Our once-defiled conscience has come alive again and sends that second thought which says, "No! Don't!"

If your mind is being renewed and filled with truth, if it's being constantly fed with the Word of God, then immediately the temptation comes the Word of God is there alongside declaring truth back to you.

''It's not right, it's a con, it's a lie, deal with it straight away like this.''

For instance, you are involved in a conversation and it begins to turn in a way you know isn't right. Immediately after the first thought of temptation calls you to add to the gossip or whatever, in comes the second thought – ''No! Walk away. Take your opportunity and get out now.''

It can be as clear as that. Get out of the situation, move away, cross the street – all ways of escape, practical openings to ensure that temptation doesn't develop into sin. The way of escape is always so practical. The second thought urges us to action. It offers you that first step in successful counterattack.

2 Timothy 2:22 is very simple and direct:

.......*Flee*............... the evil desires of youth and *pursue righteousness*

Note carefully what it *doesn't* say. It doesn't say, "Quote Bible verses" at youthful lusts, it doesn't say, "Debate the validity" of youthful lusts – it just says, "Run, get out, get away, pronto!"

Take another example. You are watching a favourite programme on television. It finishes and you just sit there a moment – just to see what's next. The programme starts and there are things there you know as a Christian are not for you. What are you going to do about it?

Do you quote Bible verses at the television? Perhaps you should get someone to hold an open copy of the latest Christian magazine in front of the screen? Hope it will go away? Prepare your confession speech now?

No, none of those things will be your second thought. Your third and fourth perhaps, but not your second! Let me tell you your second thought. It's complex theologically, it's very difficult to understand and implement, so note this very carefully.

2 Timothy 2:22

First you speak to yourself. Say to yourself, "Rise up from this chair." Tell your left leg to put one foot forward and then command, with all the power and authority given you, your right leg to do the same. Keep repeating this until you arrive in front of the television set. Now the really difficult bit. Ask your hand, right hand if you're right-handed, to move in the direction of the switch labelled "on/off". Move it in the direction of "off". Yea and verily! The television is no longer on and you are no longer tempted!

Recently many of us have found a new miracle machine – the armchair wizard. It's been especially developed for Christians who suffer temptation from TV programmes. You don't have to do all that I've just described with this machine – you just sit where you are and with one press of a button ... pouf! blank screen! Marvellous. A remote way of escape. A way to flee at the greatest pace without even getting up!

Biblical example

It's very interesting to compare David and Joseph when it comes to sexual temptation.

David stood on his roof looking down to where girls bathe. If you do that the high probability is that you will see something. Eyes are powerful instruments. What you see affects your body, your personality, your thinking. David saw. This was the moment of second thought, the moment when conscience says, "flee". But he considered. Then he enquired, then he sent for her, then he entertained her and soon it was lying and murder and scars for the rest of his life (2 Samuel 11).

Joseph had a problem. She was Potiphar's wife and she was out to entice him, day after day. One day she manipulated the situation so that she was alone with him. I bet she was at her most alluring as she propositioned him yet again. Did he say, "Hmm. This is worth considering. Perhaps a coffee and chat might help me decide?" No. The Bible tells us that he fled from her presence – he ran out of the house. He acted on his second thought and made his escape (Genesis 39).

Break the habit

Do you realize that most of our sins are habitual? We are in the habit of ignoring the way of escape and succumbing to the temptation. Very rarely is sin an isolated incident. We need to break the habit, the vicious circle of temptation and sin by hitting the point of entry again and again. Work back from the miserable fact of your sin. Work back and see where the point of entry was, the thought that was temptation. That is where you will find the way of escape, the counterattack move that nullifies the enemy manoeuvre.

Let the Word of God dwell in you richly so that you are soaked in it. It's your sword of counterattack, the arouser of conscience, the unmasker of lies. Every time Satan lies to you about all those fears and tensions, about the pleasures of sin for a season, you expose him with the truth of the Word and counterattack – fast!

Chapter 8 IMPROVING YOUR THINKING

Charismatic Cabbage or Creative Christian?

We've made our counterattack by using the sword of the Word of God, and we've responded to that nudge from our revitalized conscience. But, as we saw earlier, that isn't enough to start winning the battle. We need now to build the basis of victory from our success in the skirmish. We cannot simply stand in no man's land with our sword limp at our side, our minds in neutral, and expect to survive the enemy's next sortie!

God's aim for everyone is wholeness, not emptiness. Unfortunately, some of us as Christians have problems simply because our minds are empty. We have a very precarious foothold on success if our minds are a vacuum. Remember our verse? "As a man thinks, so he is" (Proverbs 23:7). Vacuous mind, vacuous man!

Television is the enormous entertainment success it is because so many people are actually happy to be mindless. We are a society increasingly dominated by visual stimuli, as people are content to crash out after work and absorb hours of television. Statistics on the hours children watch are frightening. It has enormous power for shaping people's thinking. As we have said before, even the general moral climate portrayed in the many soaps and comedies begins to change our view of what is and what is not acceptable.

It's not just soaps, either. For example, if David Attenborough on television says confidently that this is how things evolved millions of years ago and shows us some fascinating and beautiful wildlife, that's it for the vast majority. No further argument, end of debate – they've seen it on the telly, it must be true.

It's the same, essentially, for many people who work to a background of the radio. Switch it on, switch off the mind. Even DJs have philosophies of life that will inevitably flavour their chatter! Many of us are just mindless absorbers. We let others do our thinking for us. We don't bother to question their values or their arguments.

Many teachers will tell you how endemic this is in our children. They note that more and more students seem unable to ask the question "why?" year by year. Their minds have been in neutral. The pushbutton society has given them incredible ability to manipulate data in computer systems, for instance, but they still have to be trained afresh in the ability to think.

For those involved, say, in the media, the challenges on offer and the environment they are in is full of excitement and continuously stretching. But for us who sit at home and absorb with empty minds, with a vacuum waiting to be filled, it can be devastating to our progress in renewing the mind if we are insufficiently discerning.

This is not an issue of I.Q. levels or general intellect. This is simply about Christians taking hold of the life God has for them. Because we are born again, because we are right with God, because we have a purpose and a destiny we should be those who do not dissipate their lives in trivial pursuits and mindless inactivity. Ask yourself the question, "How creative am I?"

You can meet teenagers whose lives are computer games and television. After five minutes of conversation with you they're finished. It's not because they are naturally dull conversationalists, but they have become dull in their minds. Whatever our age, we can look at and evaluate our leisure time in the same way. Be honest: how different are you?

A hallmark of the church these days should be creativity. We should be a people buzzing with the vibrancy of our life with God. In our social lives together, in our hospitality, in our serving one another we should be rich in creativity. We should be those whose accomplishment more than matches our ability. Banish the word "potential!" Fulfil your potential in Christ!

One way forward for many of us is to read more. Uninformed Christians are so boring! Some used to read more widely and were more informed before they were born again; now they have become dull, and have "drifted down" to the general level. You were created with the ability to think, dream and imagine and to be expressive with that creativity. Get to it!

Check-up on media absorption

How many hours of TV do you watch on an average day? .....½ hr.....

Multiply by 7 and by 50 (no TV on holiday?) for hours per annum

.....175.....

Which newspaper do you regularly read?

none ☐

a tabloid ☑

a quality daily ☑

Do you ever read a world commentary magazine? ☑
(e.g. Newsweek, The Economist, Time, National Geographic)

In the last three months, tick if you have read:

a novel ☐

a biography ☑

a Christian book ☑

a Christian biography ☐

How many hours a week do you spend on average on:

sport and physical recreation? .....½..... x 50 = ...25..... p.a.

your hobby or other creative endeavour? .....3..... x 50 = ...150..... p.a.

The check-up table above is very crude. Yes, it implies judgements about the relative value of, say, TV current affairs programmes and a "good" newspaper. Of course both will be biased by their producer/editor. Nevertheless, if you were honest, it will give you a reminder about how you spend your time. And we haven't even put Bible study and prayer on it! Perhaps you would like to make an honest assessment of that, per week, too!

Fulfil your Potential

So let us purpose to make progress. How can we turn our whole thought process for good? How can we build on our counterattack and begin to fill our minds with the positive thoughts of a vibrant Christian life?

Remember Proverbs 23:7 again. If your mind is filled with Godly things you are going to start making those new Godly tracks and you're going to be more like Jesus.

So many Christians, as we have seen, are dominated by a negative, pessimistic lifestyle. They never take on new challenges or make any particularly identifiable progress. God didn't create us like animals just moving by instinct, we have the ability to create, to imagine and to achieve. Our renewed minds can open the way forward for us to fulfil our potential.

There are Christians who have paths ahead of them mapped out by God where they will be mightily effective for Him in society, but they are trapped by unrenewed minds in a vacuum of ever-present "potential". Churches are often described as having "great potential". We need to be those on a crusade to turn potential into reality.

Look at Ephesians 3:20:

Now to him who ....*is able to do*.... immeasurably more than ....*we ask*.... or ....*imagine*...., according to ....*his power*.... that is at work ....*in us*....., ...

Read it again. The reality of that verse is mind-blowing! Even as we think about things, as our minds are involved in Godly issues, so He is able to do all that we are thinking and more. As we ask things of Him, He is able to do all that we ask and more. More exciting still is that He doesn't do these things "out there", but Scripture is clear that the power is within us. He operates *within* you and me to achieve these things.

This is not the power of positive thinking. It's not will-power. It is the power of God which is fully able, and fully able to do beyond our thoughts and requests. Yes, we are limited in our thinking and wisdom, and God's ways are so much higher than ours, but there is this incredible mystery that God gets right behind our Godly thoughts and requests with His almighty power.

The object of renewing your mind is to unclutter your thinking, to clear the ground of the enemy's attacks, so that you can hear the thoughts of God in your mind. We fulfil our potential as we begin to hear and respond to the voice of God in our minds.

Review Romans 12:2:

When we are transformed from the world and renewed in our thinking we will be able to ~~test + approve what Gods will is~~ .

John 10:27 says:

"My sheep ..... LISTEN ..... to my voice . . ."

That voice is not some distant whisper we strain to hear on the wind from distant fields. It's actually quite clear and strong, but we have been cluttered up with enemy voices and the sound of battle so we have not found it easy to pick out God's voice. Get rid of the clutter and God's voice is clearer. Then the way is open for us to do and to achieve in our Christian lives above the levels we can even imagine at the moment.

Of course, you will make mistakes; know that now, get used to the idea and be ready to pick yourself up and press on. The disciples made plenty of mistakes. Jesus didn't sack them all and replace them with a new group of twelve who were more holy and more perceptive. He just corrected, encouraged and sent them off again.

Practical exercise

Next time you are praying in a small group situation, ask God to give you His thoughts about someone in your group. Don't just pray a nice evangelical prayer. Speak out what God has said in your mind.

This is not a toy to play with – this is the power of God in your life for the extension of His kingdom. We need to act on the thoughts to fulfil our potential.

I remember a lunchtime evangelistic meeting where I fell into conversation with a man who was obviously very bitter and angry and denying the existence of God. We were soon into an amazing debate about who was before God if He did exist, and whether I exist or you are a figment of my imagination, or both. How orange is this chair, what do we mean by "orange", if Adam stubbed his toe would it have hurt, etc. The whole works! But all the time a voice in my mind, a thought in my brain, is insistent. Louder and louder it came, that this man had been put out of fellowship in a church because of something he had done.

When he left, I turned to the man next to me who knew him and said:
"That was hard work, wasn't it!"

His reply left me stunned.

"Well, you know why? He was asked to leave his church five years ago because he wouldn't repent of his adultery. He went off in a storm of bitterness."

What might have happened had I acted on the thought and fulfilled my potential in that situation!

Watch Out! God at Work!

Let us back this up with another verse. Read Philippians 2:13:

For it is ...God... who works ...in you..., to ...will... and to ...act... according to ...his good purpose... .

God is at work in your mind, He is transforming your thinking. Co-operate with Him, work with Him because it is He who is causing you, as you respond, to fulfil His good purposes in you.

Many of us think God's thoughts without even being fully aware of it. Find out, reach out, step out! You will be amazed. No one can do it for you and you can't do it for others. You can't read it in a book or watch it on a video. In the end you simply have to step out yourself on what you believe God is saying to you.

What a tragedy it is that in most of our churches it is only a nucleus of people, a very small proportion of the membership who actually allow themselves to be stretched in this way. Will you join them?

There will be opportunites in homegroups, in meetings, in your street and over your garden fence. God may speak to you about people or about projects. He will teach you about circumstances and events and call you on to new things. Step out! God is at work in you and the more our minds are renewed the more confident we will become.

A person who is thinking like this is hardly mindless or vacuous – he or she is beginning to discover how improved thinking is fulfilling their potential in Christ. You will be stretched and your gifting will be both more apparent and more fruitful. Watch out! God is at work!

Review

1. Write down a couple of occasions when you know, with hindsight, that God did speak to you, but you failed to identify His voice clearly enough to step out.

   re Gibbs & God

   ....

   ....

   ....

2. What is wrong with the following statement?
   "He is able to support us to some extent in our endeavours, as long as we are not too onerous in our demands, the lines of communication between us are not too distant, and the goals we are setting ourselves approximate to His."

   God is able to do un reasonably
   more than we ask

   ....

Chapter 9   MIND YOUR MIND

We have looked at temptation, we have worked out the strategy to defeat the enemy using the sword of the Word of God and we have begun to build our transformed and renewed mind, filling it with Godly thoughts.

Now we need to maintain progress and keep our minds orientated in the right direction.   We need a minder for our mind!

The key verse is in Romans 8. Read the second half of verse 5:

Those who live in accordance with the Spirit have their ..Minds..

........................Set........ on what the ..Spirit.desires......... .

We have discovered that we can be led by God's Spirit and we have begun to see that we can have the thinking that is characterized as the mind of Christ.   The key to keeping things that way is a deliberate act of the will.

In the verse we have just looked at it is called "setting". We need to set our minds on the things of the Spirit.   It is a determination to lock onto those things.   It is as if we have brought them into focus in our aim; now we have to take a decision to lock onto the objective of the things of the Spirit, so that we are immovable.   We cannot be bounced off or diverted – we have "set" our minds.

Here is an exercise for you. What other Bible verses say similar things? Write in the full reference against the clues:

Colossians 3, verse **1**   set your heart on

..things above...

Philippians 4, verse **8**   think about such things

....

It is as if every day you are challenged – your aim and setting is given a challenge to throw it off course every morning when you wake up. Either

76

we say, "Father, thank You for this new day; I'm going to live for You and not for myself," or else we say "Oh!" – yawn – "I can't be bothered."

Setting your mind is a daily check of your aim. The decision is yours – check your setting or opt out with lethargy. There is no hotline to your homegroup leader for instant advice and encouragement. The decision is wholly yours. "Let your mind dwell on these things," says Paul. It is a deliberate, conscious act of your will. It is the minder of your mind.

Now we need to make that very practical. What are the ways in which we hold our aim, keep our minds set firmly on the things of the Spirit? I believe there are three things in our daily lives which will help us – to know the Word of God, to be a worshipper and to be supported by other Christians.

1. Set Your Mind on the Word

Here we are again, back on this crucial subject: knowing what God's Word says about us. We met it before when discussing how to rebut temptation. Here it is once more. The Spirit revels in the promises of God – so should we. If we are to set our minds on the things of the Spirit there is no doubt that that means delighting ourselves in what God has said.

Please note here what it's *not* about. It's not about floating around in a super-spiritual haze quoting Bible verses incessantly at anything and anyone. When I'm playing football I don't drift around the pitch in a holy glow of meditation. When I'm playing football I'm fully involved mentally, emotionally and physically in running, passing, tackling and (hopefully!) scoring goals. Yes, because I'm a Christian I want to play fair and play with a good attitude, but I'm going to play my guts out and be fully involved with my team.

What we're after is a mind-set that, in a sense, runs on autopilot and leaves us free to enjoy life to the full. It's not an invasion of the super-spiritual and all the unreality that goes with that sort of approach. Rather it's that we let God infuse our whole life with His thoughts and priorities so that we are just walking naturally with Him.

The Word of God is effective in many ways. Let us look at some.

a) It shows you who God is.

So many Christians have a problem because they are worshipping some-one who is, to all intents and purposes, a stranger to them. They have all sorts of problems with fatherhood, perhaps from their own childhood or from unbalanced teaching from the past.

I have met Christians who believe God is still punishing them for wrong decisions made in the past. Now the God I know isn't like that, but it's often a real battle of persuasion. They need to soak up the truth of what the Bible says about the father heart of God. That way, the God *I* know isn't like that becomes the God *they* know isn't like that because the Word of God says so.

b) It shows you who you are.

Each day it's so good to remind yourself of who you are in Christ. We need to know what our inheritance is, we need to know what our rights are, and we need to know our glorious position in Him. We are liberated from hurt and rejection by realizing how God has unashamedly adopted us.

People have all sorts of problems in these areas of acceptance – limited and wrong views of the fullness of our salvation – but you can walk out of these problems simply by believing the Word of God.

c) It develops effective discipleship.

Take a fresh look at yourself. Take a fresh look at the members of your church. As the Holy Spirit draws more and more people into the kingdom of God it will be your responsibility to disciple them. You are called to "make disciples". That is an exciting prospect for us all.

However, if you don't know the Word of God, and if your mind is not set on what He says, then what on earth are you going to pass on to others? If you haven't grasped a right picture of God as your Father in heaven, and if you are unsure about your position in Christ, you will have to stand back on the sidelines and watch others do the job of discipling new Christians.

What you are, others will become. That applies negatively as well as positively. If you do not grasp the liberating principles of the grace of God – as set out for example in another book in this series* – the chances are that you will bring people unwittingly into legalism. That's because you

*Enjoying God's Grace, by Terry Virgo (1989)

won't be sharp enough to recognize the symptoms of a legalistic attitude in yourself or in others.

Immerse yourself in the Word of God, let it fill your mind and affect your outlook and your behaviour. Then others will not need to make your mistakes – they'll make their own anyway – and they will learn from your example. That is practical discipleship.

d) It develops your contributions to the Body of Christ.

Let us look at two different verses where Paul is exhorting people to take their full part in the life of the church.

Look at Ephesians 5:18-19 and Colossians 3:16:

1. What is Paul's objective for us? What are the actions he is looking for in our life together? *Give thanks to God with his people – worshiping together*

2. There are two sources of this activity; Paul mentions one in each of the two passages – what are they?

    (i) Ephesians 5:18 *be filled with the spirit*

    (ii) Colossians 3:16 *word of Christ*

Two different routes, but the same fruit and the same result. We need both of these routes working together in us to fulfil our potential in the Body of Christ. We need to be filled both with the Spirit and with the Word of God.

See how unbalanced you become when you have one, but not the other. For instance, you may be in a meeting and the Spirit stirs you with the love of God for the people. You have been earnestly desiring to be used in spiritual gifts and as the Spirit rests upon you, you prophesy. It goes something like this:

"My people, I tell you I love you. I love you utterly, through and through, and I love you. My love is fantastic, terrific and wonderful and I love you."

Now actually there may be someone in great need of that reassurance, but, for the most part, the people there will know that truth. What will happen is that they will be edified by the heartfelt expression of that truth which they will pick up from your voice. They will recognize in their spirit the Spirit of God stirring you.

The problem is that there will be severe limitations of expression. The Spirit cannot plunge into the reservoir of your mind and stir scriptural thought in you. You will be lame and limited. Often, too, people hold back from stepping out, especially in prophecy, because they fear being shallow. There is an awareness in us that there is not much for the Spirit to work on.

Of course, when you first flex your muscles in spiritual gifts there will be a simplicity and a lack of breadth. Actually, God loves to use simplicity. But as the Word dwells in us richly more and more so our prophesying will be richer and stronger. Words and phrases start to have hints in them from all over the scriptures, bringing depth, variety and a richness which encourages, edifies and builds up the whole Body of Christ.

When the unction of the Spirit and the power of the Word come together something mighty always happens. Let it be our desire to facilitate that by devoting ourselves to what the Bible has to say.

e) It develops faith to live by.

Here is more evidence of a person whose mind is set on the things of the Spirit. You have faith to live by. The mind set on the Spirit will produce a person who is moving in the dynamics of faith, who is living day by day in the realm of faith.

Look at Romans 10:17:

There is a two-stage process described here. What is it?

(i) Faith comes from *hearing the message* &

(ii) *the message* is heard through *the Word of Christ*

Some folk have funny ideas about faith. Faith is not "believism". We do not work ourselves up into a frenzy of "believism" in an attempt to convince ourselves we have faith. Faith is actually practically the opposite of frenzy. Faith is an inner conviction, an assurance, a deep inner knowing that you have heard from God and are walking with Him.

That is a killer to intellectual pride. Having gone through all the arguments and tested out all the pros and cons we are left with a simple

80

statement: I know because I know.

"What do you mean 'because I know'?"

"Because I know that I know."

Very frustrating for the intellectual approach, but the fruit of a mind set on the Spirit and dwelling on the Word.

Remind yourself of that famous verse on faith, Hebrews 11:1:

Now faith is .....*being sure*................................. of what we hope

for and .....*certain*................................. of what we do not see.

Faith is being sure. It's not even a risk.

Some people view faith as risk. That is because we exercise faith in the realm of the unseen, the-as-yet-to-be evident. Whether it's about the great truths of Christian doctrine or about a decision in the area of guidance we are talking about an assurance of rightness, not a risk. It may look risky to those who are not exercising faith, but there is no uncertainty in your mind to give rise to any element of risk.

Some people view faith as risk because of the "stepping out" element. Stepping out requires courage and spiritual strength, but it must be built on an assurance, a certainty, about God and His Word. Faith is not believism or presumption.

Neither is it a magical formula. God is not restricted to our rules and He will often surprise us and challenge us in the way things happen. He doesn't want a lot of automatons following their noses through sets of rules; He wants a vibrant, daily relationship full of life and variety.

Our problems with faith lie in our minds. It's often a battle in the mind.

Answer honestly: when God speaks to me about something do I:

1. act on it straight away almost without thinking? ☐

2. act on it quickly with full assurance? ☐

3. act on it eventually after a period of checking out? ☑

4. receive doubts about it and battle with them first? ☐

5. usually succumb to doubts that it would happen? ☐

For most of us, most of the time, an honest tick goes in box 4, doesn't it?

For example, if someone asks for prayer for healing, the first thought is, "Great! An opportunity to see God do something here." My second thought is a doubt that anything will happen. Why? Usually because:

(i)   I'm cynical – renew the mind.

(ii) I've prayed for people in the past and nothing's happened – renew the mind with the promises of God.

(iii) I'm not sure the person himself/herself even believes anything will happen – renew the mind; it's up to God, not them.

(iv) The enemy himself doesn't want me to be effective and is flying in with the temptation to disbelieve God – renew the mind.

Martyn Lloyd-Jones has emphasized a very helpful phrase – *doubt is faith under pressure*. That is very helpful. Doubt is faith in a battle, a bit of a crisis if you like. Doubt is not unbelief. It is belief under challenge. Lloyd-Jones made another helpful statement – *doubt comes when I listen to myself rather than speak truth to myself*.

If I speak the truth of the Word of God to myself, if I proclaim His promises and His character I am encouraging the faith I already have. I am doing the opposite to allowing the doubts to dominate. I challenge doubts with the Word.

This isn't "believism" because faith is already there. The point is that the renewed mind, the disciplined mind, the soaked in the Word mind will encourage that faith into strength and action. The unrenewed mind simply wallows in doubt and indecision.

2. Be a Worshipper

A second way of improving your thinking is to nurture your renewed mind by being a worshipper. Jesus reminded us of the basis of the ten commandments in Matthew 22:37. A feature is that we are to love the Lord "with all our mind".

Paul knew what it was to have a worshipping mind. In 1 Corinthians 14:15 he tells us that his practice includes singing and praying with his mind. In reference to the previous verse, verse fourteen, he doesn't want his mind to be unfruitful in a worship context. Being a daily worshipper improves your mind. It brings clarity, perception and balance.

3. Be of One Mind

Your thinking is improved when you are not in isolation, but in fellowship with others. Submitting our thinking to one another requires humility and requires effort on our part when it would be easier to go it alone.

Look at Philippians 1:27 and Philippians 2:2 and fill in:

Stand firm in ..... *one spirit*

Contending as ..... *one man*

Being ..... *likeminded*

Having the ..... *same love*

Being ..... *one* ..... in spirit and in ..... *purpose*

What does this mean in reality? Does it mean that we all have one big brain in the middle of us, like Dr. Who's Tardis, to which we all bow down and submit? Does it mean you don't have opinions? Does it mean you lose your individuality? No, of course not. None of these "scare stories" are true to real inter-relationship and commitment.

The key to it all is that we keep our individuality, those marks of personality that are as precious to God as to us. What we lose is our independence – which is actually a curse to growth and maturity in the Body of Christ. It's interesting to note that one of the marks of a cult is that people lose their individuality as well as their independence. Of course, we want to avoid cultism, but let us not throw out the baby with the bathwater! It is God's command that we learn to submit our thinking to one another.

I have a calling on my life to be of one mind with my brothers and sisters. It's nothing to do with committing intellectual suicide or with being a moron or something like that. It has everything to do with adding in my gifts and my distinctive qualities to help build the life of the church, and letting others knock the edges off me.

Submit yourselves to one another and your thinking will be improved, there is no doubt about that. Elsewhere (Ephesians 4) Paul calls us to maintain the unity of the Spirit until we attain the unity of the faith. We are all seeking to be better representatives of Christ, aren't we? You are not the only one with that goal in mind. Take hold of humility and grasp the opportunity of being of one mind.

Review

At least one or two points in this chapter will have really struck home to you about improving your thinking. Write them out briefly:

1. _Love independence Keep_
   individual)

2. _Daily worship_

Now set yourself realistic goals for taking action which focus on the two points above. What can you do better which will bring fruit in those areas? Write down a target for each:

1. _continued fellowship_

2. _Discipline - daily_

Chapter 10   AND FINALLY – WINNING MINDS

I love most sports and really enjoy them, but if there's one sport I cannot stand it's cross-country running.   When I was in my first year at senior school we had compulsory trials for the cross-country team.   You can probably remember this experience yourself – most games masters and mistresses seem to have devised their own form of purgatory along similar lines.   The first twenty would be in the team, and, just to make it interesting, the last twenty would do it all again.

"No problem," I thought.   "At least twenty in front, at least twenty behind, easy!"   Off we set.   I kept a big pack ahead of me and a big pack behind.   No problem.   We crossed the finishing line, and, to my horror, number nineteen is yours truly!   Maths never was my strong point.

For a whole year I ran in that team.   I didn't care whether we won or lost. I learnt every trick in the book to avoid actually running, from feigned stitch to hiding in the sweet shop for a couple of laps.   I had no motivation, no determination, no desire to win.   My mind had backed out before we even started.

Some of the boys were good.   They were in with a chance every time. They would push through barriers of real stitch, pass by the temptation of slipping into the sweet shop; they wanted to give it their best, they wanted to run and they had the winning mentality.   I just didn't have the winning mentality, I was a pushover and a loser.

Look at 1 Corinthians 9:24:

Run in such a way as ...*to get the prize*............................... .

Later on (verse 26) Paul adds emphasis by saying, "I do not run like a man running aimlessly."   My aim is to see my mind renewed.   I know it's possible, I know I can win, and I am determined to do so.   I'm not going to simply roll along through life aimlessly.   I want the prize!

If I am going to run a winning race I must have this mentality.   It is crucial if I am actually going to see change in my thinking and my life. This book has taken you behind the scenes, as it were, into the backdrop to the battle of your mind. We have looked at the state your mind was in before you came to Christ and the ways in which the process of renewal takes place. We have looked at the enemy's only weapon and the way he uses it on the battlefield. We have seen how to deal with him and counterattack, and how to build a new mind set on the things of the Spirit, full of the Word of God.

Now, go for it! You have the capacity; the power at work within you is more than sufficient. Will you take up the challenge to be transformed by the renewing of your mind? Will you be a winner?

FOR YOUR NOTES

FOR YOUR NOTES

More titles in the

How to...

S T U D Y   S E R I E S

Praying The Lord's Prayer

is a practical workbook for those who want to maintain a consistent and effective prayer life, and can be used by individuals or groups. Taking Jesus' prayer structure as a model, it develops the themes of the fatherhood and names of God, the nature of God's will, reign and kingdom and His gifts and forgiveness in our lives.

Terry Virgo is based at Clarendon Church, Brighton. He also leads the *New Frontiers* team committed to planting and serving churches in the UK and overseas. He is author of *Restoration in the Church* and *Men of Destiny*.

Catalogue Number YB 9177   £1.70

Handling Your Money

is a Bible-based workbook on managing your personal finances. Beginning with the idea of God as giver, the book discusses our attitudes towards wealth, money and possessions. It contains advice on budgeting and avoiding debt, and teaches us how to be abundant givers ourselves. This workbook is suitable for both individual and group use.

John Houghton leads the eldership team at Hailsham Christian Fellowship, Sussex. His wider ministry as a speaker and writer reflects his concern for Christians to face the practical, social and moral implications of the gospel in today's world. John and his wife Janet have three teenage children. His previous books are *Hagbane's Doom*, *Gublak's Greed* and *Surin's Revenge* (for children), *The Healthy Alternative* and *A Touch of Love*.

Catalogue Number 9176   £1.70

Learning to Worship

is a devotional workbook for use by both individuals and groups who want, in the author's words, to 'appreciate from the Scriptures this magnificent gem that God has so graciously allowed us to rediscover'. Whether we are worshipping alone or among God's people, this book offers Scriptural insights to help us become the worshippers that God is seeking.

Phil Rogers is the Senior Pastor of New Life Christian Church, South Lee. He is a keyboard player and compiles the yearly songbook for the Downs Bible Week. His own songs include *Who is This?* and *How precious, O Lord.* He is also involved in teaching and training worship leaders. Phil lives in South East London with his wife Sandy and their three sons.

Catalogue Number YB 9179

£1.80